NONE FOR THE ROAD

To my very good friend Robert Stanley in appreciation of his help, encouragement and enthusiasm over many years.

NONE FOR THE ROAD

Understanding Drink-Driving

by

Ronald C Denney

B.Sc., Ph.D., C.Chem., F.R.S.C., F.R.S.M., M.I.Mgt.

"Our deeds still travel with us from afar,
And what we have been makes us what we are."

George Eliot

Shaw & Sons

Published by
Shaw & Sons Limited
Shaway House
21 Bourne Park
Bourne Road
Crayford
Kent DA1 4BZ

© Ronald C Denney 1997

Published January 1997

ISBN 0 7219 1530 2

A CIP catalogue record for this book is available from the
British Library

Printed in Great Britain by
Biddles Limited, Guildford

CONTENTS

LIST OF FIGURES

LIST OF TABLES

EXPLANATION OF TERMS

Throughout this book the word 'alcohol' is used to mean 'ethanol', the active constituent of fermented liquors.

All results and values are expressed in metric quantities and the following conversion factors may be helpful:

1 µg (microgram) = 1 millionth of a gram (used for breath alcohol levels)

1 mg (milligram) = 1 thousandth of a gram (used for blood and urine alcohol levels)

1000 mL (millilitres) = 10 dl (decilitres) = 1 L (litre)

Some countries, including Great Britain, refer to the number of milligrams of alcohol in 100 mL of blood (or urine), i.e. mg/100 mL. It may also be expressed as grams per litre (promille, ‰) or as a simple percentage (%).

So that: 50 mg/100 mL = 0.5 promille = 0.05%

80 mg/100 mL = 0.8 promille = 0.08%

100 mg/100 mL = 1.0 promille = 0.10%

Hence, the level of 0.08% in the USA corresponds to 80 mg in 100 mL in Great Britain. Throughout the book all quantities, such as 80 mg or 30 µg, are with respect to a 100 mL volume of the appropriate body fluid.

THE AUTHOR

Dr Ronald Denney is a forensic scientist who has previously worked in the chemical industry, carried out research on nicotine and amino acids in the United States and spent twenty-seven years as Lecturer and Reader in Organo-analytical chemistry at the University of Greenwich until he took early retirement in 1995. He has specialised in forensic work for thirty years with particular reference to matters involving alcohol and drugs. He has written 20 books, of which five deal with aspects of analytical and instrumental chemistry and three have previously covered the subject of drink-driving and accidents. Dr Denney is considered to be one of the country's leading experts on breath testing and alcohol analysis and is frequently consulted by solicitors in connection with drink-drive cases. He is regularly called as an expert witness and has given evidence throughout the country in Magistrates' Courts as well in Crown Courts and the Central Criminal Court. He is a member of the International Council on Alcohol, Drugs and Traffic Safety and has given numerous papers on alcohol analysis and breath and blood testing at international conferences in many parts of the world.

Dr Denney has broadcast many times on radio and television in connection with forensic subjects and is popular as a speaker at civic clubs and as an after dinner speaker on the wider aspects of forensic science.

PREFACE

Since my first book on alcohol and driving *The Truth about Breath Tests* was published in 1970, I have tried periodically to up-date and revise the information it contained. This book is the fourth of this nature, all built upon the original concept and dealing as completely as possible with problems associated with alcohol, accidents, changes in the law and testing procedures. I have always believed that it is important for scientists to be prepared to explain scientific matters as straightforwardly as possible for non-scientists and I hope I have achieved this objective on this occasion.

The whole subject is very much an international one with the same problems arising in many countries. Whilst there may not be total unanimity on how these problems should be handled, there is always a common desire to reduce alcohol and driving related accidents. This leads to legislation moving steadily forward towards lower drink-drive limits and an increased use of scientific and technical measures in law enforcement.

Whilst this book uses material from my previous books, much additional and up-dated data has been included and is intended to keep the motorist, rider and other road users informed and aware of how alcohol is likely to affect them, the undesirable results it may have and the consequences of alcohol related accidents and incidents. It deals with the origins and nature of alcohol, its role in history and society, the clearly established relationship to accidents, the growth of legislation and the procedures, instruments and devices now available for detecting people driving with alcohol in their bodies.

It is hoped that this book will continue to serve as a guide and to help and encourage drivers to act in a responsible manner with respect to their fellow citizens.

I have not set out to tell drinking motorists how to get round the law or how to produce artificially low results in breath or blood samples, even assuming that were possible. It will, however, give them some guidance about the nature and effect of alcoholic drinks and the need for self-limitation before driving motor vehicles or using potentially dangerous equipment. No doubt there will still be those who delude themselves into thinking that they can drive perfectly safely after drinking several pints of beer or a bottle of wine. Unfortunately, they will probably find their mistake the hard way and involve others in the consequences.

Perhaps I should emphasise that where I criticise either the law or public attitudes, it is intended constructively. I do feel that people in general are too blasé about the drinking driver, despite the carnage on the roads. I also feel that in many respects the law is too lax. I have tried to indicate the steps that need to be taken in order to rectify the situation and to encourage a more responsible attitude to drinking in general.

The data used in this book is not a state secret, although you might think so sometimes from the difficulties of even obtaining an international list of drink-drive limits from a motoring association. As a result, it has been culled from a wide range of sources over many years. This has meant employing information from a variety of disciplines: while I have taken every precaution to provide correct information and an accurate interpretation, I cannot accept any legal responsibility for use, or misuse, of the data in this book. Any person charged with a drink-driving offence is strongly advised to obtain a private analysis of any blood or urine sample and to seek full legal advice if he or she intends to contest such charges.

The responsibility for any errors that may have occurred in the book is mine and I shall be pleased to receive constructive criticisms and suggestions for any improvements in future editions.

I am grateful to many people and organisations for their help in either providing me with, or guiding me to, data and information. In particular, I must record my thanks to the Royal Society for the Prevention of Accidents, the Transport Research Laboratory, Lion Laboratories plc and the University of Greenwich. Special thanks go to my brother, Peter J Denney *ARIBA*, for re-drawing many of the illustrations, to Jo Bradbury for producing new photographs at short notice, and my wife for her word-processing and computing skills. They have all made my work much easier.

Remember, there is *no* safe blood alcohol level – the best advice is "Don't Drink and Drive".

Ronald C Denney

INTRODUCTION

"Drink not the third glass – which thou
canst not tame when once it is within thee."

George Herbert

The traditional invitation to the traveller to have "one for the road" is well established throughout the world and persists despite the extensive warnings about the dangers of alcohol, especially for anyone driving a motor vehicle, flying an aeroplane or piloting a boat.

The continual growth of car and vehicle ownership and the increase in distances covered, often at high speeds, is now occurring in the poorer nations of the world and is no longer just concentrated in the developed countries. The majority of people aspire to owning or having access to a car and being free to travel at will. As a result, road casualty figures throughout the world are horrendous and in any one year are comparable to those that occur in any international war. It has been estimated[1] that each year nearly 400,000 people are killed and 20 million people injured in road accidents. Whilst figures for road casualties in the technologically advanced countries are falling due to better roads, vehicle design and legislation, they are counterbalanced by increasing accident statistics as the developing world becomes more mobile.

That so much time and energy has been devoted to trying to legislate against the combination of alcohol and driving is a clear indication of the important part that drinking plays in accident statistics. At the same time there has been a much greater awareness that drinking and accidents is an international problem rather than just a national matter. Now, almost wherever motorists go in the world they will find legal limits on blood alcohol levels and the tendency is for these limits to become even tighter.

The growth in the use of motor vehicles has produced enormous problems throughout the world. It has gone hand in glove with enormous increases in populations, problems over the supply of fuels and deterioration in the urban and rural environments. The motor car, lorry and motorcycle have played their part in contributing to the destruction of the environment but have at the same time led to an enhancement in the life that can be enjoyed by many people, enabling them to escape more easily from congested cities into the countryside and to the coasts and to visit friends and relations and historical sites. The enormous expansion in the leisure industry owes a great deal to this increase in individual mobility and would be greatly affected by substantial restrictions on personal motoring.

At the same time, many normally responsible citizens reveal a completely different character once they get behind the wheel of a car or the handlebars of a motorcycle. They will disregard speed limits, drive through red lights and park in restricted areas without a thought for laws or regulations. In addition to this, some drivers become aggressive and violent, displaying what has been called 'Road Rage'. These factors, coupled with drinking alcohol and taking drugs, can only contribute to road accidents. However, these same drivers consider themselves badly treated if the police devote any effort to reducing the number of traffic infringements and think it is immoral of the police to use radar traps to catch speeding motorists or road blocks to check the roadworthiness of vehicles. But if a similar number of deaths and maimings to those resulting from road accidents were caused in a single day by terrorism, industrial accidents or aeroplane accidents, there would be a public outcry, much of it from the self-same road users who so frequently disregard even the most sensible of rules and recommendations.

Under these circumstances, it can come as no surprise that in almost every country the introduction of roadside breath tests has met substantial opposition on the grounds of infringement of personal liberties. As for the taking of blood or urine samples, these have frequently met similar opposition on the grounds of being invasive or destroying privacy. There is often a total failure to appreciate that to obtain and retain the privilege of driving a high-speed, heavy-weight piece of machinery, there are also important attendant responsibilities – not the least of which is that the driver should seek to avoid being a danger to other road users.

To those who have watched the road accident figures with mounting horror, it has seemed incredible that it should have taken so long for legal blood alcohol limits to have been accepted in the major motoring countries. Yet, when the Road Safety Act 1967 came into operation in Great Britain, there was widespread protest about oppression of the motorist and claims of impending bankruptcies amongst publicans. Similarly, in the USA, the introduction of the state laws led to objections based upon the famous fifth amendment to the US Constitution. This stipulates that no person "shall be compelled in any criminal case to be a witness against himself ....", it being argued that the provision of a breath or blood sample constituted self-incrimination. The same type of constitutional issue has arisen in other countries and has generally had to be overcome by what are known as 'implied consent laws' based upon statutes that specify that any person operating a motor vehicle shall be considered to have given his consent to such tests where reasonable grounds exist for assuming he has been drinking.

If such laws represent an infringement upon the liberty of the individual then it may equally be argued that this is necessary, for the liberty of the individual only exists in so far as it does not interfere with the corresponding liberty of other people; in this case to enjoy the safe use of the road.

Only a small proportion of motorists can really be classified as being blatantly irresponsible and these are inevitably involved in a totally disproportionate number of accidents and traffic offences. All too often the motorist charged with a drink-drive offence is also found to have paid no road tax, to have an untested car with bald tyres or lights which do not work and to have parked in a restricted area. However, since all motorists have often been made to feel that they are enemies of society, because of congestion, parking problems and pollution

involving motor vehicles, it is no wonder that they are suspicious
and resentful when additional restrictions and controls are
imposed upon them. Nevertheless, responsible motorists will
always co-operate with any reasonable approach for reducing
accidents if they are convinced of its value and purpose, as has
been the case with the introduction of the compulsory wearing
of seat belts. To achieve this co-operation, it is essential that
road users are well informed at all times, not only about new
laws which have been enacted but also about the reasons for
those laws. All too often society uses a bludgeon when what is
needed is education.

I have watched with interest the enormous increase I predicted[2]
many years ago actually take place in the use of scientific
methods of law enforcement by the police and in the growth
of work in the forensic science laboratories. These have in
turn led to more private forensic scientists and a better
structured system to advise and assist the defendants in cases
involving scientific and technical matters.

The enormous expansion in the use of electronic machines
for both roadside screening and evidential breath alcohol
testing led to the false assumption that these could totally
replace other proven methods of analysis. As a result, the
police have frequently been placed in very difficult situations
because of the nature of some of the laws that have been
enacted. At the same time, the ordinary citizen has been
misled into believing that such 'new-fangled' devices are
inaccurate and unreliable and the legislators have had to go
away and rewrite some of their laws.

It is important to appreciate that medical and scientific studies
have clearly shown that alcohol plays a much greater role in all
forms of accidents, at home, in industry, in the air and on
water, as well as on the roads than was originally believed to
be the case fifty or sixty years ago. Much of this research is
wrapped up in technical journals which the average person is
unlikely to read. Because of this, it often appears only in the
form of a small paragraph of statistical data in newspapers.
But it is the understanding of the role that alcohol plays in

accidents that makes the difference between being able to enjoy alcohol in a social context and abusing it and oneself as a problem drinker or alcoholic.

It is important to remove the mystique from the chemical and medical data to help people to appreciate the enormous risks they present to themselves, their families and to other people from irresponsible drinking of alcohol. Of course, there will always be those who think they know all the answers or who continue to disregard the warning and the law. However, the history, production, effects, use and general study of alcohol are fascinating and have led to the creation of a vast industry inter-linked with national economies, organised crime, legislation and religions. Alcohol has an influence, directly or indirectly, on everyone, but in the realm of drinking and driving the results and consequences are often only too obvious.

Chapter 1

ALCOHOL, ITS ORIGIN, USE AND ABUSE

"And lately, by the Tavern Door agape,
Came stealing through the Dusk an Angel Shape
Bearing a Vessel on his Shoulder; and
He bid me taste of it; and 'twas – the Grape!"
The Rubaiyat of Omar Khayyam – stanza 42

Alcohol has been extolled and reviled in literature ever since human beings could write, and Omar Khayyam certainly appears to have looked upon it as a means of escapism. In the forms of wine, beer or spirits, alcohol has been known and used by most societies for centuries. At the present time, production and distribution of alcoholic drinks is a major industry in most countries, the source of many jobs and the provider of substantial revenues through excise duties and taxes. The use and abuse of alcohol has led to conflicts between those who would restrict or ban its use and those who believe it serves as an acceptable safety valve against the pressures of modern living, as a socially acceptable drug. But where the balance lies between the personal enjoyment of alcohol on the one hand and the burden placed upon society by more extreme indulgence leading to crime, violence and accidents on the other is not always easy to define. No other substance has been so lauded in verse and song or criticised so frequently as has alcohol. The product from the fermentation of fruits and vegetables has been used as a medicine, an anaesthetic, a soporific and, above all, in various forms as a social drink. But as well as giving pleasure it has also led to great distress, caused the break-up of marriages and been responsible for some appalling tragedies.

Although the preparation of alcoholic drinks has been known for centuries, the isolation of the active constituent, ethanol, in a pure state was probably not achieved until the 12th century AD[1]. This was because it is always difficult to separate the alcohol completely from water when it is produced by fermentation.

Large quantities of pure alcohol (ethanol) are now manufactured by industrial processes but it can always be produced by fermentation of any substance containing sugar, or from more complex chemicals such as starch which can be broken down into sugar, and the discovery of this process has been lost in the mists of time. There is even sufficient sugar in mare's milk for fermentation to take place to make kumiss or kefir from cow's milk. However, the fermentation process is not usually capable of producing alcohol at a greater strength than about 15–18% by volume and home wine-makers frequently find difficulty in making wines with an alcohol content greater than 10–12% by volume.

It is very likely that the first discovery of alcohol was made by prehistoric man who found some long-standing grape juice had developed a unique flavour and produced an exceptional physiological effect. There is every indication that almost all ethnic groups and civilisations, except the Eskimos, have had recourse to their own forms of 'fire water' or 'moonshine' for ceremonial occasions and to celebrate victories. It is believed that alcohol from fermented fruit juices was the first painkiller employed by prehistoric man[2] for tooth extractions and minor operations.

This practice continued for many years, and it is highly probable that Samuel Pepys' draught of liquorice, marsh-mallow, cinnamon, milk, rose water and white of egg had a high alcoholic content to prepare him for his ordeal[3] of a bladder stone operation in 1658. Even now, alcoholic solutions are still employed for disinfecting wounds and sterilising instruments and surfaces in the absence of more effective chemicals or procedures.

Abuse of alcohol

In most countries of the world alcohol is a socially accepted drug. Despite this, those countries in which the drinking of alcohol is permitted also have laws controlling the behaviour of drinkers in an effort to limit the harm and damage that might be done due to people being intoxicated. This dichotomy that exists in modern societies also occurred in ancient civilisations in which the preparation and consumption of alcoholic beverages can be traced back for at least 8000 years. The early Chinese, Greeks, Egyptians, Aztecs and Romans all had their own forms of fermented products. They often created well-established and co-ordinated industries such as the wine production in Egypt more than 4000 years BC where there existed an organised system of vineyards linked with the caravan routes and commercial outlets[4].

The production and consumption of alcohol in the Middle East continued to be important until the growth of Islam in the early 7th century AD. But as a result of the strong anti-drinking view of that religion, very little alcohol is now produced or consumed in most of those countries in which Islam is the predominant religion. This has a direct influence on nearly 20% of the world's population. As one author expressed it[5], "Islamic states take a rather spoilsport view of alcohol though those with a colonial hangover or an important tourist trade may be more pragmatic."

The inebriating effect of alcohol has also been well documented over the centuries. An Egyptian treatise on etiquette published more than 3500 years ago (Figure 1, overleaf) advised people not to boast of their drinking prowess as beer could make them incoherent and drunk. Alcoholic liquor was also well known in early biblical times, Noah being the first person recorded as suffering from drunkenness as a result of drinking wine from his own vineyard[6]. The Holy Bible also records one of the earliest uses of alcohol for immoral purposes when Lot's daughters made their father drunk in order to have sexual intercourse with him in the hope of conceiving to perpetuate the family line[7].

It is unlikely that the early wines of the Chinese and the Egyptians had very much in common with modern products as the maturing process now used could not be carried out in the traditional leather bottles. It was not until glass and

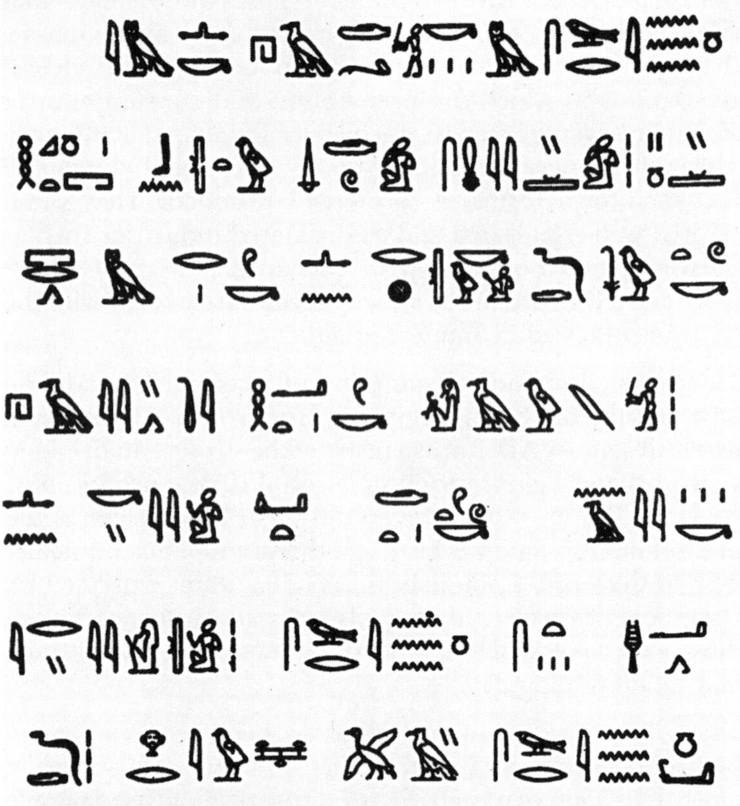

Don't boast about your drinking ability,
Two jugs of beer and even
You don't know what you are saying:
If you fall and hurt yourself
Nobody offers a hand to help you.
And your drinking companions,
Still standing, say "Away with this drunk!"
If anyone comes looking to question you,
They find you lying on the ground,
As if you were a little child.

Figure 1 – 'The Wisdom of Ani'
*(from a papyrus of the twenty-second dynasty). Translation of part
from the reproduction in* Medical News, *14 January 1974.*

ceramic bottles with corks were employed that different approaches to fermentation and ageing occurred[8]. The expansion of the Roman Empire throughout Europe and around the Mediterranean 2000 years ago brought wine and the spread of viticulture to many countries.

However, excessive drinking of wine increased and was greatly encouraged to assist in raising revenues by successive Roman emperors, including Caligula and Claudius. A reaction to this occurred in AD81 when the Emperor Domitian ordered half the vineyards to be destroyed as one of the earliest measures to control alcohol consumption. There is no evidence to suggest it was very successful and throughout Europe the variety of alcoholic beverages available increased as conquering hordes took their own knowledge and traditional beverages with them into other areas. For instance, mead, which is prepared by fermenting honey and adding spices for flavouring, was introduced into Britain by the Saxons. So until the middle of the 17th century, the common alcoholic drinks were cider, ale, mead and wine.

Although distillation of wines was probably known to the Greeks and Romans, the strong alcoholic liquids produced did not gain popularity until about the 16th century. At that time spirits were recommended by monks for medicinal purposes and this led to increased leisure drinking of the distilled products of wines in France and Germany during the 17th century. Many of the famous cognac producers were founded in France during the 18th century and their products are rigorously controlled and supervised to maintain their quality and reputation.

Regional beverages

Throughout the Middle Ages, the maintenance of vineyards and the production of wine was virtually a church monopoly in Europe as the wine was required for communion services[9]. The distillation of spirits and preparation of liqueurs were developments from this which are still frequently associated with ecclesiastical settings. But distillation of fermented liquids does not produce pure alcohol. The process actually gives rise

**Figure 2 – Distillation of spirit of wine in the early
sixteenth century.** *From the title page of* Das Buch Zu
Distillieren, *H Brunschwick, Strasbourg, 1519.*

to a water/alcohol mixture known as an azeotrope. The alchemists were, therefore, unable to produce pure alcohol. However, wine and the spirit of wine (aqueous alcohol) were used by them and were considered important enough to warrant their own alchemical symbols. They probably found the solvent properties of the 'spirit of wine' of value in preparing their various chemical concoctions.

Alchemical Symbols

Wine　　　　　　　　　　　　*Spirit of wine*

The growth of California and Australia as major wine producing areas is fairly recent but viticulture was first established in Britain during the Roman occupation and existed continuously through to the early part of this century. Even after the dissolution of the monasteries, Henry VIII preserved the vineyards and wine-making flourished. In more recent years, the art and skill of growing vines and making wine have been revived as the British taste for wine has developed. Many new vineyards now exist in southern England, mainly in East Anglia, Kent, Sussex and Hampshire where average summer temperatures above 10°C can be expected. The largest of these vineyards is about 100 hectares (250 acres) in size. However, Italy and France remain the world's largest wine producers and consumers, both exceeding consumption of 100 litres per head per annum, although the average wine consumption throughout the whole of Europe has dropped in recent years[10]. In comparison, Poland, Hungary and the USA have the highest per capita consumption of spirits, while Germany, the former Czechoslovakia and Belgium head the beer-drinking league table.

Direct comparisons of the consumption of alcoholic beverages are difficult due to the range of drinks available and national preferences. Because of this the international league table is best expressed in terms of litres of alcohol drunk per head of population[11]. However, to be really fair, this should be based per head of population over the age of, say, 16 years, as few countries encourage or condone drinking by the young. As Table 1 shows, there are striking differences in the amount of alcohol drunk, with the USA predominantly a beer and spirits country, falling at the bottom of a list headed mainly by countries with relatively high wine consumption levels in addition to beers (or lagers) and spirits.

Table 1

Total Alcohol Consumption per Person by Country 1990 (Litres of pure alcohol)

1	Luxembourg	12.3
2	France	11.9
3	Portugal	11.6
4	Germany	10.9
5	Switzerland	10.7
6	Hungary	10.5
7	Spain	10.4
8	Austria	10.3
9	Denmark	9.9
10	Belgium	9.4
11	Czech Republic	8.6
12	Greece	8.6
13	Italy	8.4
14	Netherlands	8.2
15	New Zealand	7.8
16	Bulgaria	7.8
17	Australia	7.7
18	Argentina	7.5
19	Cyprus	7.5
20	Ireland	7.4
21	United Kingdom	7.4
22	Finland	7.4
23	Poland	7.1
24	Canada	7.1
25	USA	7.0

Most countries have tended to take an ambivalent attitude towards alcohol, on the one hand accepting it socially and gastronomically, while on the other surrounding its sale and use with restraints, limitations and taxes. Warnings against the dangers of alcohol are common and one of the most frequently used quotations[12] against excessive drinking is Solomon's "Wine is a mocker, strong drink is raging and whosoever is despised thereby is not wise". Similar cautionary advice abounds elsewhere in literature but is balanced by an equal number of statements in praise of wine or beer and extolling their virtues. But very little can equal the enthusiasm of Howell[13] who wrote ".... good wine makes good blood, good blood causeth good humours, good humours cause good thoughts, good thoughts bring forth good works, good works carry a man to heaven, ergo good wine carrieth a man to heaven." Obviously, nobody could have defined an easier route to salvation!

The whole nature of alcohol and its effects makes it an obvious subject in many plays and was a feature which Shakespeare drew on extensively in *King Henry IV* in describing the social life and drinking habits of Falstaff and his friends in the Middle Ages[14]. However, Shakespeare was well aware of both advantages and disadvantages of consuming large quantities of ale, particularly upon the sexual proclivities of the drinker. His views were clearly expressed through the Porter in *Macbeth*[15] with the statement that drink "provokes and it unprovokes; it provokes the desire, but it takes away the performance: therefore, much drink may be said to be an equivocator with lechery; it makes him and it mars him." The same can be said about drinking and driving; while alcohol makes people believe they can drive better it will, in fact, mar and undermine their driving performance.

Alcohol as a narcotic

Because of the social problems associated with alcohol, it is correctly classified as being a drug and is usually included in books dealing with synthetic and natural drugs. Both alcohol and tobacco are narcotics, possessing an ability to induce drowsiness or stupor, the word narcotic being derived from

Figures 3 and 4 – Hogarth's 'Gin Lane' (left) and 'Beer Street' (right).
(Both reproduced by courtesy of the trustees of the British Museum [© British Museum].)

the Greek *narkotikos*, meaning to be numb. In its action alcohol is considered to occupy a position intermediate between the addiction forming and the habit forming drugs. Its worst feature is undoubtedly its ability to cause alcoholism, with all that means in terms of debility, degeneration and physical deterioration.

It is because of the debilitating effect of alcohol and its tendency to loosen moral responsibility that there have always arisen powerful anti-drink groups wherever alcohol production has existed. Prohibition of alcohol is normal in Hindu and Islamic cultures, and this has been strongly underlined in recent years when European workers in Saudi Arabia have received whippings and imprisonment for breaking that country's laws against the production and sale of alcoholic liquor.

Abstinence is also a major feature of the Methodist and Baptist denominations as well as the Christian Scientists, Seventh-Day Adventists and Mormons. In many instances, legislation over licensing hours and the strength of alcoholic drinks has been greatly influenced by pressure from religious authorities.

Until the end of the seventeenth century, the consumption of spirits in Britain was small in comparison with other alcoholic drinks. But in 1690 the process of distillation, which had been a Crown monopoly, was made available for private exploitation. This was done in order to assist agriculture by creating a market for corn. At about the same time, licensing of ale houses was introduced but this did not apply to the sale of gin which had the added advantage of carrying a very low excise duty. As a result, sales of gin increased nearly tenfold to about six million gallons per annum by the mid-eighteenth century[16].

Controls and prohibition

The excesses resulting from the cheapness of spirits gave rise to substantial public commentary, of which the most famous is Hogarth's engraving *Gin Lane* (Figure 3). By comparison *Beer Street* (Figure 4) was intended to represent a greater level of sobriety and social acceptability. The conditions expressed in *Gin Lane* ultimately led to the Gin Act of 1736 in which a prohibitive tax, at that time, of 2s 6d (12½p) was imposed on every pint of spirit. The result of the Act clearly showed the dangers of going from one extreme to another as it led to riots and had to be repealed, through being inoperative, in 1743. Since that time sales of beer and spirits have been treated in the same way and no campaign for prohibition has succeeded in Great Britain, although voters in Dundee elected the only successful National Prohibition party candidate, Mr E Scrymgeour, to Parliament from 1922 to 1931.

The extreme difficulties involved in imposing any form of prohibition in a democratic country were made very clear in the USA. What became known as the 'Noble Experiment' started in 1920 following the passing of US Constitutional Amendment XVIII during World War I[17]. However, state and county options on being 'dry' had already existed before this[18]. The only real result of 'the experiment' was an enormous growth industry in the production and distribution of illicit liquor, and tacit acquiescence of the bootlegging criminal fraternity by a large section of the drinking community. Not until 1933, after President Hoover had appointed a commission following the St Valentine's Day massacre and other serious crimes, was the amendment repealed. This returned the responsibility for any form of control to the states and led, as before, to enormous differences between states, many of which exist to this day. This ambivalent attitude in the USA continues with most states having legislated lower drink-drive limits for young drivers compared to older drivers.

Although most countries have become less extreme in their attitudes to alcohol over the past 30 years, such that alcohol taken in moderation is considered socially acceptable, there is still considerable concern about the general increase in drinking and of alcoholism, particularly amongst young and under-age drinkers. However, there is no single point at which one goes from being a light social drinker to a regular drinker and later to becoming a problem drinker or alcoholic. The change is frequently a gradual one over a fairly long period of time and occurs without the drinkers, and often those around them, being fully aware of it. But while the light social drinker does not necessarily have an alcoholic drink every day, and then only one or two half pints of beer or single whiskies, the moderate drinker may have two or three pints of beer and the heavy drinker will be up to five pints of beer each day or about five double whiskies. A person drinking more than this is well on the way to becoming a problem drinker and is in serious need of help. This is why it is a mistake to assume that drink-drive limits should be high enough to catch just the heavy drinker. The heavy drinker was probably once a moderate drinker and prior to that a social drinker. The object of a drink-drive limit is to have an enforceable level which will ideally deter *all* drink-driving.

Delusion and illusion

Ethanol, the alcohol associated with commercial alcoholic drinks, is not the only substance of this type which is used and abused by problem drinkers. Methanol (also called methyl alcohol or wood alcohol) is chemically very similar to ethanol but is much more toxic. Despite this it is drunk by 'meths drinkers', most commonly in big cities, although it is unpleasant and causes digestive pains and partial blindness in the short term and complete blindness and death if taken regularly. Other alcohols which are available in various commercial forms are propanol and ethylene glycol; the former is used as a solvent and the latter as the main active ingredient of anti-freeze. They are both dangerous and potentially toxic and should never be used as substitutes for ethanol (alcohol). Ethylene glycol is very similar to the diethylene glycol found to have been added illegally to some Austrian wines in 1985, supposedly to make them sweeter[19]. However, these particular alcohols do not arise naturally to any significant extent in normal alcoholic drinks produced from traditional fermentation procedures.

In many ways it is the general lack of awareness of the dangers from the use and abuse of alcohol that makes it so difficult for legislators, road safety officers and social workers to get people to establish a balance between their personal pleasures and their responsibilities within society. Fortunately, increasing efforts are being made on radio and television, and by public and voluntary bodies, to inform and educate people about the perils of heavy drinking. In many countries there are increasing pressures to control the advertising of alcoholic drinks, especially at sporting events, on television and in publications read by young people. This is because the implication is given that it is healthy and beneficial to drink these products.

Alcohol is a great deluder – it makes you feel strong when you are weak, it makes you feel capable when your abilities are diminishing and it leads to over-confidence. There are more old wives' tales about drinking and driving than about practically any other everyday activity. Inevitably, hardened drinkers will always claim that they drive better after two or three pints than they did before, and conversely teetotallers may believe that a half-pint a night makes you unfit to drive the following day.

Although only a minority of drivers at any one time have a significant quantity of alcohol in their blood, it is certain that a large proportion of motorists have driven or do drive at some time when their blood alcohol level is too high. In many instances this is done out of ignorance. All too often the motorist asks "What is a safe amount to drink?" and usually receives an unhelpful answer.

Although the best advice will always be "Don't drink and drive", if it is not a government's intention to completely prohibit drinking prior to driving, it is essential that better guidance be given to the majority of people who have no wish to be a menace on the roads but who would like some indication as to how much they can reasonably consume. Partially as a result of increasing legislation against the drinking driver, more and more governments and voluntary organisations are becoming aware of the need to educate the drinker about the potential dangers of even moderate amounts of drink. In the last ten years many more health education documents, films, and radio and television programmes have been produced dealing with the long-term effects of alcohol and advising people on the amount of alcohol in different drinks.

However, most drivers still do not know what the legal limit means in terms of numbers of drinks, or how long it takes for alcohol to be burnt up in the body so that it is safe to drive.

Alcoholic content

There is still considerable confusion over the manner in which the alcohol content of drinks is expressed. Nowhere has this confusion been greater than in Great Britain which has traditionally used 'original gravity' for the strengths of beers and 'degrees proof' for spirits. To make matters worse, 'degrees proof' in the USA differed substantially from 'degrees proof' in Great Britain. The standardisation brought about by the European Union in presenting all strengths in terms of percentage alcohol by volume (abv) has gone a long way to clarifying the situation. On the continent of Europe this approach is often called the Gay-Lussac system (GL), although it is not uncommon to hear people now refer incorrectly to the abv as 'percent proof'. To the layman the traditional terms gave no real guide to the relative strengths of beers or spirits but served as a beautifully archaic way of working out excise duties.

The full extent of the variation and conflicts that existed can be appreciated from the fact that proof spirit (in Britain) was originally defined[20] as the lowest concentration of ethanol in water which, when put on to gunpowder, would still enable the gunpowder to be ignited. As proof strengths for aqueous solutions of alcohol (ethanol) are still used for industrial purposes, it is important to point out that 'proof spirit' is now[21] expressed as being an aqueous solution of such a concentration that its weight is $^{12}/_{13}$ that of an equal volume of water, measured at $51\,°F$ ($10.6\,°C$). In the USA proof spirit is an aqueous solution containing 50% of ethanol by volume at $60\,°F$ ($15.6\,°C$).

Pure ethanol is about 175 degree proof spirit (GB) or 200 degree proof (USA). An approximate conversion of proof values and per cent ethanol by volume can be obtained from Figure 5.

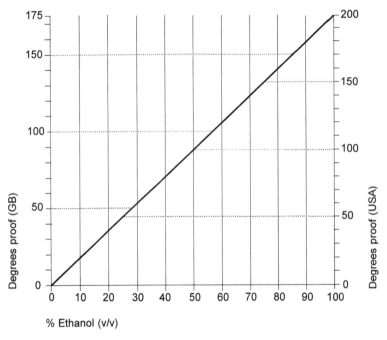

Figure 5 – Relationship between proof values and ethanol concentration.

From this it can be seen that the USA proof value can be obtained by multiplying a British proof value by $^8/_7$. The abv can be obtained from British proof values by the equation:

$$abv = \text{degrees proof} \times {}^4/_7$$

Different countries hold widely varying views about what constitutes an alcoholic drink. Under the prohibition laws in the USA, an intoxicating liquor was considered to be one containing over 0.5% of alcohol but for many years in Great Britain a drink was considered to be alcoholic if it contained more than 1.14% abv. This meant that weak alcoholic drinks such as shandy (beer plus lemonade) could be sold as 'non-alcoholic' to those not old enough to purchase full strength alcoholic drinks. Much of this confusion has been sorted out by the Licensing (Low Alcohol Drinks) Act 1990, which required the percentage alcohol content (by volume) to be marked on all drinks containing more than 0.05% alcohol, and only drinks with less than 0.5% alcohol to be sold in unlicensed premises to children.

Types of drinks

There is, of course, an enormous variation in the types of alcoholic drinks and the amount of alcohol they contain[22].

Beer, which is the most widely consumed alcoholic drink in Britain, Australia and the USA, is produced by fermentation of malted barley in water with the addition of hops or chemical flavouring. In Germany wheat beers are also made. Initially, the malt is sieved, crushed and mixed with hot water to form a mash. The liquid from the mash, called the wort, is then mixed with hops and often additional sugar. After filtration and cooling the fermentation takes place using strains of the yeast Saccharomyces cerevisiae to transform the sugar into alcohol. The eventual alcoholic content depends upon the initial sugar concentration and the extent to which fermentation is allowed to proceed. During the fermentation process a foam is produced and the yeast floats to the surface (the process being known as top fermentation)[23]. Beers produced in this manner usually contain between 2–5% of alcohol (by volume) although stronger ales, such as barley wines, may contain more than 10% alcohol.

Lagers are made by a slightly different process known as bottom fermentation. In this procedure a low temperature, only slightly above freezing, is employed and the yeast sinks to the bottom of the fermentation tank. The final product, which is a light yellow colour, contains about 4–6% alcohol (by volume) and has a milder flavour than most beers. In some cases alcohol contents of brews are increased by partially freezing the solution and removing some of the ice formed by the water.

Non-alcoholic and low alcohol beers and lagers (NABLABS) specially manufactured for motorists and teetotallers are made either by removing the alcohol by distillation from a normal fermentation product or by stopping the fermentation before it has progressed very far[24]. There are very conflicting reports about the tastes and qualities of NABLABS but they do have an important role to play in road safety. The specially made non-alcoholic beers and lagers contain as little as 0.05% abv and the legally defined 'low alcohol' drinks range from 0.5% to 1.2% abv. Studies have shown[25] that with an alcoholic strength of 0.5% abv it is not possible to drink the lager fast enough in sufficient quantities to produce a positive blood alcohol level. Even with low alcohol lagers of about 1.0% abv, a positive breath alcohol value of less than $10 \mu g/100$ mL is produced by a man of average weight 70 k (154 lb) even when drinking three pints within one hour, or by an average weight woman (57 k, 126 lb) drinking two pints in that time.

Cider, made from fermentation of apple juice, is one drink which varies enormously in its alcohol content and for this reason its effect on people tends to be unpredictable. Although most commercial forms of cider contain less than 5% alcohol, some of the local brews in Somerset, Devon and parts of France may have as much as 10–12% alcohol. Local rough or 'scrumpy' ciders can have devastating effects on the unaware drinker. The corresponding drink prepared from pear juice, known as perry, is less common but equally potent.

Wines are obtained as the fermentation products of the sugars of grapes, the different colours and flavours depending very much on the type of grapes employed, the land on which the vines were grown, the extent of the fermentation and the age of the wine. Wine connoisseurs, of course, assess the quality of a wine by a large number of factors, particularly the 'bouquet' and taste to the human palate.

For general purposes wines are divided into three main groups:

1. Table wines, such as Hock, Moselle and Burgundy, are produced as a result of spontaneous fermentation from the yeasts on the surface of the grapes. They contain 6–15% alcohol. Most countries keep very tight controls over the quality of wines manufactured and the regions for producing particular types of wines are carefully delineated, as under

the appellation controllée law in France. Even then the quality may vary greatly from one year to another depending upon the summer weather, which also contributes to the claims for any particular 'vintage'.

2. Sparkling wines such as Champagne and Asti Spumanti, in which there is a substantial carbon dioxide gas pressure in the bottle, have undergone a second fermentation within the bottle after being corked and wired. As a result, the alcohol content can be 15–18%. With poor quality sparkling wines, the secondary fermentation is replaced by bottling under carbon dioxide gas pressure.

3. Sherry, Madeira, Port, Marsala and Vermouths are classified as 'fortified wines' as they are made by adding spirits, such as brandy, to the natural wines before being further matured. They possess alcohol contents within the range of 15–22%.

It should be emphasised that the flavour of a wine depends very much on the nature of the minor components and other fermentation products which have been formed. There are several hundreds of these and not all have been identified. However, chemical analysis of wines using gas chromatography has shown that particular wines produce their own characteristic 'chromatographic fingerprints' which can aid in their identification and the detection of impurities or adulterants.

Spirits are obtained by distilling the liquids obtained from natural fermentation. Under normal conditions, spirits for sale in Britain should comply with section 3(4) of the Food and Drugs Act 1955 and be a minimum of 65 degrees proof (37% alcohol). Of the many spirits available, brandy is the blended distillate from grape wine, gin is the distillate from maize and rye fermentation, rum is obtained by distilling fermented molasses and malt whisky is a blend of distillates from fermented malted barley. Vodka is often referred to as a neutral spirit and is very popular with miscreants who derive pleasure in 'lacing' other peoples' drinks. It is a virtually tasteless and odourless liquid obtained by distillation and charcoal filtration of the products of grain fermentation.

Liqueurs such as Cointreau (orange flavoured), Crème de Menthe (mint) and Tia Maria (coffee) are produced by adding different natural and synthetic flavours to a base liquid of nearly neutral grain alcohol. Others, including Drambuie and Wild Turkey Liqueur, are spirit based, flavoured by herbs with honey and/or fruit flavours. Alcoholic contents of liqueurs can be as low as 15% or as high as 50%, although normally levels between 20 and 40% are to be expected.

Table 2

Guide to the Alcohol Content of Various Alcoholic Drinks

		% alcohol by volume	*Normal bar measure (mL)	Weight (grams) of alcohol per measure
SPIRITS	Brandy, Gin, Rum, Vodka, Whisky	35–45	25	7–9
LIQUEURS	Cherry Brandy, Drambuie, Tia Maria	25–40	25	5–8
FORTIFIED WINES	Port, Sherry, Vermouths	15–22	50	6–9
CIDERS*	Commercial Rough	3–6 Variable 5–15	250 500	6–2 10–30
BEERS*	Barley Wines Lagers Export Ales Light Ales Mild Bitter	9–11 4–6 4–5 $2\frac{1}{2}$–4 $2\frac{1}{2}$–4 $2\frac{1}{2}$–5	 250 500	18–22 8–12 8–10 5–8 5–8 5–10

* The pint (568 mL) and half pint (284 mL) are still permitted in the United Kingdom under European Union rules. The US pint is $^4/_5$ of the UK pint.

An indication of the approximate alcohol content of groups of drinks is given in Table 2. It should, however, be borne in mind that the variation in the alcoholic strength of beers and lagers is much greater these days compared with a few years ago, since the return to 'Real Ale' and strong local brews. Also, the table can give no guide to the strength of either home-made beer or home-made wine. Some of these are highly potent and should be treated with respect and considerable caution.

Illicit drinks

Illicit spirits, such as 'poteen' from Ireland and 'moonshine' from the Appalachian states of the USA, often contain very high levels of alcohol and can also be lethal due to lead impurities arising from solder used in the manufacture of illicit stills. The inherent dangers in consuming such substances greatly exceed the financial benefits from the evasion of excise duty.

In addition to the various alcoholic drinks available for human consumption, it is also possible to purchase the main constituent 'ethanol' in various forms for industrial and domestic use. Such substances as 'rectified spirit', 'industrial methylated spirit' and 'mineralised methylated spirit' all contain other natural and synthetic chemicals which make the alcohol unsuitable for human consumption.

It should be borne in mind that the laws on drunkenness and blood alcohol levels are only concerned with the actual effects and concentrations of alcohol, they do not discriminate in any way between the sources of the alcohol. It is, for instance, not uncommon to find low background levels of alcohol in the blood of people who normally consider themselves to be teetotallers. This can arise as result of using certain types of vinegar and from drinking fruit juices, all of which may contain small quantities of alcohol.

Alcohol as a danger

Until the advent of the industrial revolution and the manufacture of motor vehicles in the second half of the 19th century, the drinker was normally of no great danger to the community outside his own family circle. However, the development of high powered machinery and of motor driven transportation automatically meant that there was a much greater danger of the drunken person involving others in an accident.

For many years alcohol was looked upon favourably as being a tonic or medicine as well as something to help people relax and socialise. Whilst it is still seen in this context, there is a also a far greater awareness of the dangers arising from even moderate quantities of alcohol as well as from its abuse and from alcoholism. However, there is no internationally agreed definition of alcoholism[26] or of what constitutes excessive drinking. Despite this, estimates show that in Great Britain there are more than three million people addicted to alcohol whilst the corresponding figure for the USA is often put at well above 10 million. It has been claimed that alcohol misuse in Great Britain costs industry £2 billion per annum and imposes a burden of £150 million on the National Health Service. In fact, despite all the very serious worries about other drugs such as cocaine, heroin and amphetamines, alcohol is the most seriously abused drug in the world.

Related to this is the prevalence of associated crimes including assaults, house-breaking, shop-lifting and rape. Alcohol has been found to be a major contributory factor in acute general hospital admissions and is a substantial feature in accident and emergency admissions, especially at night time. Many of the hospital admissions are due to traffic accidents of which a high proportion are alcohol related. However, the true figures for the involvement of alcohol in incidents of all types are not known as there is no scope for obtaining breath or blood samples in most cases, either at hospitals or at police stations, except in autopsies or possible drink-drive offences.

Prior to the introduction of chemical tests for blood alcohol concentrations, accused motorists could be released or prosecuted on the basis of any subjective observations of a medical practitioner who in many instances was half asleep through being woken up in the middle of the night. The difficulties of proving intoxication on the results of limited physical and practical tests were quite obvious for many years[27]. As a result, it was uncommon to obtain a conviction for 'drunk in charge' when blood alcohol levels were below 125 mg and even at levels about 200 mg successful convictions were only obtained in about 45% of the cases.

Despite the obvious problems in employing subjective testing, the examination for inebriation carried out in British police stations until 1967 was based upon a modified form of tests originally published in a British Medical Association report *Tests for Drunkenness* that had been produced in 1927. It included various tests of walking in a set direction, writing tests and the ability to add and subtract numbers. However, even now it is quite common for police in various countries and states to subject those they have apprehended to lengthy interrogations when they are clearly unfit to give acceptable coherent answers due to alcohol or drugs. If a person is over the legal limit and therefore unfit to drive, use machinery or carry out a precision activity due to alcohol, then he or she should be considered unfit to answer more than the statutory questions on being arrested and tested. There is certainly some justification in requiring the breath testing of all arrested suspects prior to interrogation to ensure that they are fit to be questioned. This would certainly overcome the problem of defendants answering questions and then seeking to invalidate the replies at a later date on the ground that they were too intoxicated to provide valid answers.

Evidential tests

While Britain was still making drunks walk along chalk lines, other countries were moving rapidly towards a more scientific approach to the drinking driver. In Europe scientists were developing tube and bag alcohol testing devices and in the USA pioneering work on determining blood alcohol levels based upon breath alcohol was carried out by Dr E Bogen[28] as early as 1927. This in turn led inventors to develop apparatus that could easily be operated by police to enable on-the-spot tests to be carried out. The first successful apparatus, the Drunkometer, put the USA far ahead in the field of investigating drunken driving.

As long ago as 1965, the most frequent sample medium for *evidential* alcohol tests in the USA was breath[29], but in Europe breath tests were almost entirely used only for screening purposes and it is only during the last 15 years that roadside breath tests have become a standard feature in the motoring world.

Despite the fact that sophisticated breath testing devices had been developed in the USA prior to World War II, the British Medical Association was still trying in the 1950s to make people aware of the fact that it is not necessary for a driver to be blind drunk to be incapable of controlling a motor vehicle correctly. And it was not until the Road Traffic Act 1962 was passed that any real progress was made in Britain. By that time roadside breath tests had become a common feature in European countries like Sweden and Germany, and by 1957 Sweden had already reduced its legal limit down to 50 mg from the 150 mg level first legislated in 1941.

Most of the pioneering advances in the study of drinking and driving and the development of automatic breath alcohol analysis equipment have taken place in the USA. However, during the 1980s the use of this equipment extended round the world and such instruments are as common now in Australia, Great Britain, The Netherlands and Japan as they are in the states of the USA.

Chapter 2

ALCOHOL IN THE HUMAN BODY

"He is a drunkard who takes more than
three glasses, though he be not drunk."

Epictetus

Many people become very upset if you tell them that in drinking alcohol they are taking a drug, believing that a drug is really something dreadful like LSD or heroin or chemicals prescribed for medicinal purposes. But a drug it is: it affects the central nervous system and influences a person's mental and physical states. However, it differs from other drugs in that it is taken in large quantities compared to other drugs and is fairly rich in calories, providing about 200 calories (837J) per ounce (7.1 calories [30J] per gram). As little as two pints of beer can provide about 300 calories – nearly one-eighth of the daily energy requirement for an average person. The result is that really heavy drinkers, consuming five pints of beer or more each day, obtain a major proportion of their daily energy needs from alcoholic drinks and require a correspondingly smaller amount of food. One consequence of heavy drinking is a diminished appetite for food and an impairment of the digestive processes[1]. The calories in alcohol have, however, been called[2] 'empty calories' as they lack the nutritional balance of proteins, vitamins and minerals which are so essential for a balanced diet. This in turn leads to changes arising in the liver due to its major role in alcohol metabolism. Malnutrition of the body is likely to be further aggravated by more alcohol causing inflammation of the digestive system which in turn will impair the absorption of any nutrients which might be available from food which is eaten[3]. The overall result for the heavy drinker is cirrhosis of the liver, a weakened heart and a decayed brain.

Liver damage
Symptoms of liver damage can occur in males from regular

ingestion over several years of fairly moderate amounts of alcohol such as would occur with anyone taking six half-pints of beer or six single whiskies every day. For females only half these quantities will have the same effect. This means that a person does not need to be regularly drunk for physical deterioration to start to occur. Degeneration of this type is, of course, long term and in the case of progressive alcoholism is frequently compounded by personal neglect.

At the same time, it is not just the liver which is affected by alcohol. As most drinkers are aware, even the short-term effects of alcohol on the body functions are not necessarily all instantaneous; some faculties appear to deteriorate before others, although all are dependent upon the rates of absorption, distribution and elimination of the alcohol in the body.

Effects of alcohol

It is well known that alcohol in moderate quantities affects different people in a variety of ways. While it makes some people feel sleepy or depressed, others become relaxed, light-hearted and less inhibited. This is because, contrary to popular belief, alcohol is not a stimulant but is medically classified as a depressant. This classification is because it affects those parts of the brain which are concerned with self-control and judgement. One consequence is that inhibitions tend to be weakened due to the influence of alcohol and this may reveal itself in different forms. Thus, at a party, some drinkers may become easily excited, flushed, garrulous or sexually uninhibited, and their moods will change depending upon the amount of alcohol they have drunk. While a small quantity may make them relaxed, a larger amount may make them quarrelsome.

Absorption and elimination

Absorption of alcohol into the blood stream occurs partially through the walls of the stomach and mainly in the upper part of the small intestine once the contents of the stomach have passed through the pyloric valve. The metabolic breakdown of a small amount of alcohol also occurs in the stomach due to the presence of low levels of the enzyme alcohol dehydrogenase (ADH), but eventually most alcohol is destroyed due to ADH in the liver. When the alcohol is in the blood stream it is transported around the whole body and becomes distributed throughout the body tissues in proportion to their water contents. As a result, the highest concentrations of alcohol develop in those tissues possessing the greatest proportions of water. Because the brain has a high water content, any alcohol starts to affect the central nervous system within a matter of minutes after it has been consumed. After the peak blood alcohol level has been attained, the total alcohol level of the body will slowly diminish, if no further alcohol is drunk, and the content of the various tissues will drop in proportion to each other, maintaining what is called a 'dynamic equilibrium'.

After drinking has ceased, the maximum blood alcohol level may be attained between 30 and 60 minutes later. By then the destruction of the alcohol in the body is occurring at a fairly constant rate. The liver is primarily responsible for breaking down the alcohol, with approximately 95% being metabolised to carbon dioxide and water[4]. Unreacted alcohol is excreted through the kidneys in the urine and to a much lesser extent in perspiration and breath. Consumption of additional drinks leads to a topping-up condition and, if taken closely together such that intake is faster than elimination, will mean a progressively increasing blood alcohol level during the whole of the drinking period.

If taken on an empty stomach, 90% of the alcohol in a single drink is absorbed after about 60 minutes but the rate of absorption is greatly dependent upon the concentration of alcohol consumed and whether or not there is food in the stomach. Even with no food to slow it down, it may actually be well over an hour before the alcohol is completely absorbed and passing around the human system by transfer between tissue, blood and urine. Alcohol taken with a meal or on a full stomach is absorbed far more slowly than that taken on an empty stomach. It may, in fact, be several hours before all the alcohol has been absorbed and as a result the peak blood alcohol concentration is much reduced compared with the same amount of alcohol taken on an empty stomach. This is due both to the alcohol being diluted by the stomach contents and also because food components tend to line the stomach and delay the passage of the alcohol through the pyloric valve to the small intestine where absorption of the alcohol is most rapid. The highest rate of absorption occurs on an empty stomach with drinks containing about 20% alcohol, and with carbonated drinks such as gin and tonic.

The rapid transfer of alcohol to the body fluids has been observed in nursing mothers breast feeding their infants. Babies may receive their first taste of alcohol from the mother's milk if she drinks beer, wine or spirits as it is detectable in the breast within 5–10 minutes after being consumed[5]. In the case of mothers who are heavy drinkers there is always the possibility of the baby developing early signs of alcoholism at a young age. The danger of the transfer of undesirable substances via human milk is not restricted to alcohol and it has been known for babies to be affected by other drugs in the same way. For exactly the same reasons, pregnant women must always take great care over the amount of alcohol they consume and the drugs they take as these can be transferred through the placenta to the developing foetus. Babies have been born who have almost immediately shown signs of suffering from withdrawal symptoms, as well as being more likely to suffer physical abnormalities or retarded development. Like smoking, alcohol during pregnancy should be avoided.

Distribution

Distribution of alcohol between the various body tissues reaches a constant state about one hour after consumption of alcoholic beverages ceases. This constant ratio, of a progressively decreasing amount of alcohol, is maintained until it has all been eliminated. After the delay of one hour, it is possible to determine the alcohol content of almost any part of the body by the analysis of a sample taken from just one part of the body. Thus, an accurate measure of alcohol in the urine can be related to a corresponding value for blood and a similar value for breath.

As a result of a number of investigations[6], it is generally accepted that urine contains about 1.33 times the amount of alcohol as does an equal volume of venous blood taken from the same subject at the same time. Because of this, where legal limits for urine and blood alcohol levels are specified, the urine alcohol level is always higher than the blood alcohol limit, so that in those cases in which the blood alcohol limit is 80 mg/100 mL, the corresponding urine alcohol level is 107 mg/100 mL.

Breath alcohol

The reason that this relationship can also be extended to breath is because there is a continuous interchange between any alcohol in the blood and the air taken into a person's lungs. Anybody who has been drinking will exhale a small quantity of alcohol with his breath as long as there is any remaining in the blood stream. A volume of exhaled breath from the depth of the lungs will contain $\frac{1}{2300}$ of the amount of alcohol in an identical volume of blood. As a result, by using chemical or electronic devices to measure the alcohol content, it is possible to relate the breath alcohol level to the corresponding blood alcohol level. This ratio may actually vary[7] by about 10% between subjects and other ratios usually within the range $\frac{1}{2000}$ to $\frac{1}{2500}$ are used in various countries employing breath alcohol analyses. Rather than convert breath alcohol levels into the equivalent blood alcohol values, it is now more common for a specific legal limit for alcohol in breath to be applied. That corresponding to the 80 mg/100 mL level for blood is 35 μg/100 mL (micrograms per 100 millilitres) of breath.

In theory at least, it is possible to obtain a corresponding alcohol level by analysing any of the other body tissues and fluids, and in the USA some of the states do permit saliva to be given as a sample for analysis. The ratios for the distribution of alcohol in the parts of the body are given in Table 3, although precautions do need to be taken in the interpretation of results[8] as such values are highly variable if the alcohol distribution in the body has not reached equilibrium.

Table 3

Distribution Ratios for Ethanol between Whole Blood and Other Body Fluids and Tissues

Tissue	Factor
Whole blood	1.00
Cisternal spinal fluid	1.10
Urine	1.33
Saliva	1.18
Plasma or serum	1.15
Brain	0.85
Liver	0.90
Kidney	0.83
Alveolar breath*	0.000435

This breath alcohol figure is based upon the relationship that one volume of blood contains the same amount of ethanol as do 2300 volumes of alveolar breath (the normal range of values is between 2000 and 3000 volumes).

Blood and urine alcohol

It must also be borne in mind that, although alcohol is absorbed into the blood stream very rapidly after consumption, it is not normally detected in the urine until about 15–30 minutes later. So the urine alcohol level is lagging behind the blood alcohol level. At this stage the urine in the bladder differs from the other body fluids in that it is not in a dynamic state; the alcohol content is not changing as a result of body metabolism and redistribution between tissues but only due to more urine with alcohol at different concentrations entering the bladder. During this period alcohol levels in samples of blood and urine will bear little relationship to each other. From this point of view a breath alcohol measurement is more reliable as it should be representative of the blood alcohol level at all times during both the absorption phase and the elimination phase of the alcohol cycle.

While alcohol is still being consumed, no constant ratio between body fluids and tissues can be attained. As a result, the blood alcohol figure during consumption is higher than the corresponding urine alcohol figure. The relationship between blood and urine alcohol levels has been investigated in some detail[9] and the absorption/elimination curves (Figure 6) have been found to be of a similar shape but with the urine alcohol curve reaching a higher maximum and being displaced in time.

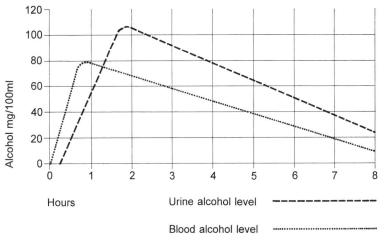

Hours   Urine alcohol level   − − − − − − − −

Blood alcohol level   ···

Figure 6 – Relationship between urine and blood alcohol levels.

From these it is clear that it is not until about 1–1½ hours after the final quantity of alcohol has been consumed that the figures for blood alcohol and urine alcohol are at all comparable; and only then if the bladder has been previously emptied. If the drinker's bladder has not been emptied prior to, or during, the course of the drinking session, a sample of urine taken for analysis is likely give a low alcohol figure. This problem is overcome in testing by discarding the first sample of urine and taking a totally fresh second sample about half an hour later to use for the analysis. It would, however, be fair to say that urine samples are only fully accurate if the drinker's bladder has been emptied at frequent intervals during the course of the drinking session.

However, considerable doubt has been cast upon the general validity of the 1.33 ratio[10,11] used in comparing blood and urine figures. It has been shown that this is really an average of very widely differing ratios rather than an absolute value. Because of this, urine samples should only be taken in those cases in which there is a deep personal objection by the motorist to providing a blood sample. It is because of the criticisms that arose over the use of urine samples for alcohol analysis that impetus was added to the developments in instrumental methods for breath alcohol measurements.

The great advantage of breath analysis is that so long as a sample of deep lung air is obtained, then the alcohol content of the breath should be truly representative of the alcohol content of the blood and there are no time delay factors such as those that affect the use of urine samples. This is because the breath alcohol content arises from direct interchange with the blood alcohol in the capillaries of the lungs, although, as discussed in Chapter 6, there are other factors which affect breath alcohol analysis and which have to be considered.

The well known balloon and tube breath testing devices that are still employed as roadside screening procedures in many countries are not accurate enough for conclusive evidential measurements that can serve as the basis for police prosecutions. Developments in electronics and computing technology have led both to the development of greatly improved electronic roadside screening instruments and to more substantial machines which are used to obtain breath alcohol results that may be presented as quantitative evidence in court proceedings. Breath testing for evidential purposes is now a well established procedure in many countries as far apart as the USA, Australia, Great Britain and Northern Ireland and New Zealand.

Even the use of blood samples for establishing a legal limit has met with some opposition on the basis that the alcohol content may vary depending upon whether it is taken from the arteries, the veins or the capillaries. This variation is likely to occur mainly during the time that alcohol is being continuously consumed and to disappear after drinking has ceased, when the alcohol cycle passes from the absorption phase to the elimination phase. By the time whole blood samples are taken for chemical analysis, the equilibrium state will have been reached so that this temporary variation does not invalidate the tests.

It has, however, been shown[12] that other discrepancies may also exist in the alcohol content of venous and capillary blood. In a series of samples taken from volunteers who had consumed various quantities of alcoholic liquor, it was found that the alcohol was not evenly distributed between the plasma (the liquid part of the blood) and the red blood cells (the solid part of the blood), so that the plasma tended to show a higher alcohol content than did the red blood cells of the blood sample as a whole. As the alcohol content of the breath is dependent upon the alcohol content of the blood plasma in the capillaries rather than that of the blood cells, it has been suggested that alcohol in blood plasma figures should be used in place of the present figures for complete blood. This would mean re-expressing an 80 mg value for complete blood as 92 mg if plasma alone was used, as the alcohol ratio between the two is 1:1.15. However, there has been no support for this suggestion but it was one of the reasons that legislating governments have chosen to specify a legal limit for the breath alcohol level rather than to measure the breath alcohol level and then to convert it into a corresponding blood alcohol value before deciding whether to prosecute or not. The whole procedure avoids numerous legal complications and potential defence arguments in court as the prosecution is made on the directly measured breath alcohol value. Similarly, the blood samples are taken by hypodermic syringes from veins rather than squeezed from pin-pricks from capillaries in the thumb or ear-lobe, as the latter might produce plasma-enriched samples.

Myths and legends

The fact that the pharmacology of alcohol varies so much from one person to another and is to a certain extent unpredictable has led to a large number of myths in connection with how much a person can drink, how to sober up rapidly, how to recover from the after-effects of drinking, and even how to fool breath or blood testing.

It is not uncommon for slightly inebriated people to undertake some form of vigorous exercise in an effort to wear off the effects of the alcohol in their blood. The most likely result of such efforts, usually carried out late at night, is to be arrested as a suspect person or for being drunk and disorderly. Unfortunately for the drinker, even swimming 1000 metres or running 5 kilometres in 25 minutes leads to no significant change in the rate of alcohol decrease[13]. Similarly, it has been shown[14] that the drinking of large quantities of black coffee is of little value as a procedure for sobering up people who are drunk. The coffee can in no way affect the quantity of alcohol that has passed into the blood stream; what it will do is to dilute down any alcohol remaining in the stomach so that its absorption into the blood stream is slowed up, although psychologically it may delude drivers into believing they are capable of driving due to the stimulating effect of the caffeine. It is, however, quite true that drinking on an empty stomach is likely to lead to much higher alcohol levels than drinking either on a full stomach or on one containing fatty foods as these line the stomach and slow down both the absorption in the stomach and the transfer to the small intestine.

The elimination of alcohol that occurs due to metabolism in the liver involves enzymes in using oxygen dissolved in the blood to break down the alcohol through various biochemical stages. The rate of conversion is not likely to be increased by any noticeable extent as a result of a little short term exercise.

It is unlikely that the human system is ever completely free from alcohol even after total abstinence from intoxicating liquors. Numerous investigators have shown the presence of small quantities of alcohol within the range 1–4 mg in blood samples taken from temperate subjects[15]. It is believed that these occur mainly from the fermentation in the body of fruit juices and from eating fruit or foods prepared from fruits.

Alcohol elimination

Although very high blood alcohol levels can be produced in a very short space of time as a result of heavy drinking, the rate of recovery from these levels tends to be slow and at a fairly constant rate for any particular individual. However, very few generalisations ever apply uniformly to all people. It is, therefore, to be expected that as the members of the human race come in various shapes and sizes they also eliminate alcohol at different rates. Because of this it is only possible to give approximate values as a guide to the decrease of alcohol in the human body after drinking has ceased. Consequently, it is normal to make all estimates with reference to the average man of 70 kilo (roughly 11 stone – 154 lb) or the average woman of 57 kilo (roughly 9 stone – 126 lb). Various studies show that such a person is capable of eliminating something between 8 and 12 grams of alcohol from the body every hour[16]. This wide variation exists simply because habitual drinkers are frequently capable of metabolising the alcohol more rapidly than are abstainers or very light drinkers. The body and liver of the heavy drinker apparently adapt themselves to some extent to the need to break down large quantities of alcohol on a regular basis, although the strain put on the body eventually leads to other medical disorders; but it does mean that the conditioned drinker is likely to recover much more quickly from the same amount of drink compared with the infrequent drinker.

In numerical terms, the normal rate of alcohol elimination corresponds to a reduction of the blood alcohol level within the range of 10–25 mg (or 4.5–11 µg for breath) for every hour after drinking has ceased. For the purpose of carrying out calculations on predicted alcohol levels, it is normal to use an elimination rate of 15 mg (6.5 µg) per hour for the average person[17]. A high rate of burn-up of alcohol obviously works very much to the advantage of any motorist who is a marginal suspect at the time a roadside breath screening test is given as he may be below the legal limit by the time he provides an evidential breath sample at the police station[18]. Even longer delays frequently occur, to the motorist's advantage, if a police surgeon has to be called to take a blood sample and this was one of the arguments in favour of the introduction of the less time-consuming evidential breath testing. Conversely, anyone giving a blood sample that exceeds the legal limit when analysed was in all probability well above that level at the time the screening breath test was applied. The only exception to this would be if the breath test was taken a few minutes after the last drink when the blood alcohol level was still rising.

One other factor that should be borne in mind is that anyone reaching a 200 mg or higher level during an evening's drinking finishing at midnight or later may still have a blood alcohol level above the legal limit by the following morning at the time they drive to work.

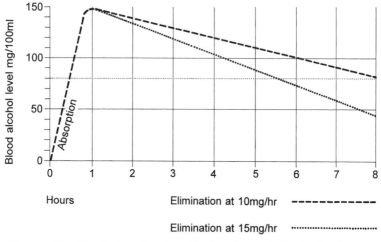

Hours   Elimination at 10mg/hr   - - - - - - - - - - -

Elimination at 15mg/hr   ·······························

Figure 7 – Variation in the elimination of alcohol relative to metabolic rate.

The relationship between the absorption and elimination phases of the blood alcohol curve is illustrated in Figure 7, and the slowness of the recovery from a high blood alcohol level can clearly be seen even in the case of an elimination rate of 15 mg every hour. The ability of people to assess their own abilities decreases as the blood alcohol level increases and drinkers are usually very poor judges of their own rates of recovery. They will also frequently assume that they are more capable of driving than is actually the case[19] and will have a totally false idea of when they may have recovered sufficiently to be back below the legal limit. It is because of this false self-assessment by drivers that many successful prosecutions for driving while over the legal limit have been made on motorists who have not been drinking for several hours; and it is possible for really heavy drinkers to be above the legal limit for as along as a day and a half after their last drink.

Toxicity

Unfortunately, most people ignore the fact that alcohol is a highly toxic drug and when drunk in sufficient amounts can kill. Blood alcohol levels in excess of 225 mg have been known to be fatal, although the mean toxic limit is generally considered to be about 400 mg. People have recovered from blood alcohol levels greater than 500 mg such as might be produced by the rapid consumption of a full bottle of whisky[20].

Much of the ability to recover from large quantities of alcohol depends upon the age, size and experience of the drinker. Inexperienced drinkers will easily succumb to lower levels and there have been some very unpleasant deaths arising from teenagers trying out a variety of drinks in a very short space of time[21]. Unfortunately, people, particularly those just discovering alcohol, are rarely warned of the possible lethal effects. In many countries there has been a considerable increase in information and education as well as evocative advertising in order to encourage drivers to take a more responsible approach to drinking[22].

In their publication, *Recognition of Intoxication*, published in 1954, the British Medical Association included a table converting the values for blood alcohol levels into the corresponding number of pints of beer or measures of whisky consumed that would be the minimum possible to give that particular value. This table was later considered to be unreliable as the blood alcohol level depends upon the circumstances under which the drink is taken and because it was felt that the table would encourage people to drink up to the legal limit. The later BMA publication, *The Drinking Driver*, published in 1965, omitted the table for these reasons.

Guiding the motorist

Traditionally, governments have been unprepared to give any real guide to drinkers as to when they are likely to go over the limit. This has been justified on the basis of "If you drink don't drive" which is by far the best policy to follow at all times. However, it cannot be ignored that once a specific blood or breath alcohol level has been defined for the purposes of law enforcement, there is an automatic assumption by the general public that so long as their alcohol levels are below these limits then it is safe to drive and above these levels it is dangerous to drive. Under these circumstances, it is irresponsible to give no guidance to drivers who will drink to some extent in any case. Failure to do this ignores the possibility that those who have not been drinking heavily and do not know where they stand relative to the legal limit are quite likely to be persuaded to take 'one for the road' because they have a false idea of what is required to exceed the limit. If guidance is not to be given, then the only real answer is to have a legal limit of zero and everyone will know that they cannot take the risk of drinking at all.

Fortunately, governments and departments of transport have started to move away from this short-sighted policy and there is increasing guidance now being given to motorists in various countries. This is often done in conjunction with health authorities who are also concerned with the broader aspects of drinking, alcoholism and the medical costs of road accidents. However, any approach of this type must be very carefully considered. The British Government found that its Christmas 1984 drink-drive campaign was totally misunderstood and misinterpreted when it used the slogan 'Stay Low', implying that motorists *could* drink and drive while giving no guidance to what 'stay low' actually meant for the individual driver. Eventually it was re-interpreted as 'don't drink and drive', but not before authorities in various areas of the country decided not to use the national campaign slogan.

In any guide to responsible drinking, allowance must always be made for the circumstances under which drinking has taken place and the period of time over which it has been spread. Obviously, someone consuming three double whiskies in half an hour is going to achieve a higher blood alcohol level than will someone else drinking six single whiskies over two hours. It is usual to express such figures with reference to our average 70 kilo (154 lb) man or 57 kilo (126 lb) woman; the same amount of alcohol in a lighter person leads to a higher blood alcohol level and in a heavier person to a lower level. In calculating recovery times it is best to err on the side of caution and only deduct 10 mg from the level for every hour that has passed since drinking started.

The 'safe' level

Direct comparisons of the quantities of various drinks required to exceed a particular legal limit are difficult to make due to the very wide variation in alcoholic strengths. Because of this there has developed a system based upon 'units of alcohol'. A unit of alcohol was originally expressed as a volume of alcoholic drink containing 10 grams of alcohol. That was later revised down to 8 grams. It was then recommended that to avoid medical disorders arising from drinking, men should drink no more than 21 units in a week and women only 14 units. It is also claimed that a single unit corresponds to:

— a single public house measure of spirits (25 mL)
— a public house measure of sherry (50 mL)
— a glass of wine
— half a pint of beer or lager.

On the same basis, a pint of beer or double whisky are both equivalent to 'two units of alcohol'.

However, 'units of alcohol' must be treated with extreme caution. Whilst the alcohol content of 8 grams is roughly correct for the measures of spirits and sherries or ports, it can be a long way out for wines and beers. A public house or restaurant measure of wine is often 150 mL and if that contains 12% alcohol then the so-called unit actually has more than 14 grams of alcohol in it. In the case of beer the unit of alcohol only corresponds to a half pint (284 mL) containing 3.6% alcohol, so beers and lagers at 5.0% actually contain more than 10 grams of alcohol in the same volume.

Four units of alcohol (two double gins or two large sherries) taken within a short period of time on an empty stomach can be sufficient to put some people at the British legal blood limit of 80 mg within about 30 minutes. In Great Britain it has become common for road safety workers to advise male drivers who feel it is impossible to avoid drinking to stick to the 'Rule of Three' – three single measures of whisky or three half pints of beer. For women a 'Rule of Two' is much safer. In countries and states operating a 50 mg limit, the 'Rule of Two' should apply generally.

The fastest rate of 'safe' continuous drinking for a period of seven hours works out to be one unit of alcohol every hour: equivalent to $3\frac{1}{2}$ pints of beer from start to finish. With this rate of consumption there should be virtually no increase after the initial rise in the blood alcohol level for an average man. This is possible because the elimination of alcohol from the body is occurring at roughly the same rate as the absorption of alcohol into the body. However, it must be emphasised that drinking at a faster rate than this will lead to a progressive increase in the alcohol level in the body and ultimately to the legal limit being attained and exceeded.

Table 4

Alcohol Consumption and Maximum Blood and Breath Levels

Alcohol level (Average man)				Alcohol level (Average woman)	
Blood mg/100 mL	Breath μg/100 mL	Beer (3.6% abv) pints (568 mL)	Whisky (40% abv) 25mL measures	Blood mg/100 mL	Breath μg/100 mL
17	7	$\frac{1}{2}$	1	26	11
34	15	1	2	51	22
50	22	$1\frac{1}{2}$	3	77	33
67	29	2	4	103	45
84	37	$2\frac{1}{2}$	5	128	56
101	44	3	6	154	67
118	51	$3\frac{1}{2}$	7	179	78
134	58	4	8	205	89
151	66	$4\frac{1}{2}$	9	231	100
168	73	5	10 ($\frac{1}{3}$ bottle)	256	111

Table 4 gives the approximate blood and breath alcohol levels resulting from the drinking of normal strength beer (3.6% alcohol by volume) or single measures of whisky by the average man weighing 70 kilo (154 lbs). The volumes are reduced by approximately 40% (i.e. to three-fifths of the amount) to produce the corresponding values for the average woman of 57 kilo (126 lb).

Because women require so much less alcohol to put them over the legal limit, it is necessary for them to be even more cautious about their drinking than men. It also means that it may not always be wise for the drinking husband to have his apparently more temperate partner drive the car home. If they go to a party or the public house together, the only really safe thing to do is for them to leave the car at home or for the driver not to drink at all.

The values in the table represent the maximum levels possible from these quantities of drink and do not allow for alcohol burnt up in the body. They do mean that a man who gives a blood alcohol value of 84 mg/100 mL or breath alcohol reading of 37 µg/100 mL must have drunk *at least* 2½ pints of beer or the equivalent amount of other alcoholic drinks, and had probably consumed much more than that amount.

Widmark and calculations

One of the most useful, and misused, developments in the field of alcohol pharmacology has been the equation and constants developed by Professor Erik Widmark in his pioneering work on alcohol concentrations in humans carried out from 1922 onwards[23]. He produced a formula which made it possible to calculate the *theoretical* maximum blood alcohol level that could arise from the consumption of a known amount of alcohol in the form

$$a = c \times p \times r$$

where:　　**a** is the mass of alcohol drunk
　　　　　c is the maximum blood alcohol level (per cent w/v)
　　　　　p is the weight of the drinker
　　　　　r is a constant (the Widmark Factor) to allow for the water content of the body.

Widmark found that for men the value of **r** was 0.68 and for women, with a lower water content and higher proportion of fat, it was 0.55. However, these values are averages and whilst applicable in general calculations for people of proportionate height and weight may differ by 10% or more for people who are substantially over or under weight.

So for a man weighing 80 kilos (176 lb) drinking three double whiskies (150 mL) containing 40% alcohol by volume, the maximum theoretical blood alcohol value would be:

$$c = a \times {}^{100}/_p \times r \equiv 47.4 \times {}^{100}/_{80} \times 0.68 \equiv 87 \text{ mg}/100 \text{ mL}$$

A similar calculation for a 55 kilos (119 lb) woman drinking two double whiskies would be:

$$c = a \times {}^{100}/_p \times r \equiv 31.6 \times {}^{100}/_{55} \times 0.55 \equiv 104 \text{ mg}/100 \text{ mL}$$

The corresponding breath alcohol values are obtained by dividing by 2300, i.e. 104 mg in blood $\equiv$ 45 µg/100 mL in breath.

In practice, values lower than the theoretical figures are obtained as people normally drink over extended periods, rather than all at once. So some alcohol is eliminated from the body before peak values are attained and the rate of alcohol absorption may be slowed due to the presence of food in the stomach.

Calculations of this type can be used to obtain an idea of what a person's blood or breath alcohol level may be some time after drinking has ceased. But allowances have to be made for alcohol elimination as well as different human physiologies leading to variations in the actual Widmark Factor used. Procedures for taking these aspects into consideration have been developed[24] to provide more accurate values for **r**, especially for overweight and obese people.

Slowing down the absorption

Alcohol levels are effectively reduced if the alcohol is taken with a major meal or after the stomach has already been filled. Substances which line the stomach and slow down the transfer of the food into the small intestine will lead to lower alcohol levels. There is strong evidence to support the popular belief that a pint of milk drunk before taking alcoholic beverages will help to maintain a low blood alcohol level. Investigations carried out at Queen Elizabeth College, London University[25], showed that the milk led to a 50% reduction in the average maximum concentration of blood alcohol. This work was used as the basis for a large scale marketing campaign for milk. The experimental figures, however, only applied to subjects in whom the maximum blood alcohol level was about 40 mg.

The extent of the effect of any dairy product on keeping the blood alcohol level down depends greatly upon its fat content. A more detailed study showed[26] that a pint of milk taken before drinking leads to a 25–30 mg reduction in the blood alcohol maximum, a pint of cream causes a 35–40 mg reduction and a pint of yoghurt is best with a 50–60 mg reduction. They all act by coating the walls of the stomach and slowing down the rate of absorption of any alcohol. The same effect is found if drink is taken while eating a large meal and it has been found that particularly low blood alcohol levels are attained if drinking is carried out after eating fish and chips[27], due to the combined effects of the fat and food in the stomach.

Alcohol and drugs

It cannot be stated frequently enough that any combination of alcohol with other drugs is unpredictable in its potential action. While many regularly prescribed drugs appear to have no enhanced effect with alcohol, there are also many that do and the only correct action is not to drink alcoholic drinks when taking drugs of any type. In an effort to increase public awareness about drugs which are a hazard when in combination with alcohol and driving, Norway introduced a regulation that all drugs in this category must carry a red triangular label[28]. That drugs by themselves, and in combination with alcohol, are a growing problem in connection with traffic accidents is evident from almost every relevant study. One investigation in Tennessee, USA[29], showed that in studies on injured drivers over a period of five months, 37% gave positive blood alcohol level results and of these more than half were also positive for drugs. In many cases two or more drugs were identified. Similar studies in other parts of the USA and other countries have shown that a high proportion of people driving under the influence of alcohol have also taken prescribed or illegal drugs. Many of these drugs, such as cannabis, barbiturates, diazepam and temazepam have a sedative effect which is greatly increased in the presence of alcohol. A typical view expressed by one expert[30] is "joint exposure of humans to alcohol and barbiturates is potentially very deadly". Under these circumstances, the chances of being involved in a fatal accident can be considered to be astronomically high. There are no general rules that can be given about alcohol/drug interactions as they all differ – the only guideline must be don't mix them, even if you are not driving.

Intoxication remedies

With the increase in blood and breath testing of motorists, there has been an obvious potential market for any manufacturer who can make a product which will either prevent the absorption of alcohol or speed up the drinker's rate of recovery. Whilst most of these are based upon sound scientific principles, it is doubtful if they have any real effect if used in the quantities recommended by the manufacturers.

One such product is the charcoal/kaolin pill which is intended to prevent intoxication by coating the lining of the stomach with kaolin to slow down the absorption of any alcohol, while at the same time reducing the amount of free alcohol by absorption of some of it on the charcoal. It is unlikely that one small pill will have much effect upon a person who drinks enough to go over the limit, although it might have a small effect at low blood alcohol levels.

It is, however, well established[14] that large doses of fructose fed either intravenously or orally to intoxicated patients lead to increased rates of recovery from the effects of the alcohol. This type of treatment is used especially with patients who are suffering from head injuries in addition to the possible toxic effects of the alcohol. This principle has been used as the basis of a wide range of tablets and sobering-up drinks containing fructose and vitamin C. The advertisements for these products fail to point out that for these to have any effect, the drinker must take between 100–200 grams of the fructose and the time taken to sober up is still several hours for people with blood alcohol levels at about 200 mg. The prospect of drinking half a pint of concentrated fructose solution on top of any major amount of alcoholic drink should be enough to put most people off the idea as any benefits must be considered to be questionable to say the least, especially in view of the fact that it is likely to cause abdominal pains and diarrhoea.

A drug has been discovered that will overcome the feeling of drunkenness and the undermining of inhibitions. Unfortunately, it does not reduce the blood alcohol level and can increase the likelihood of convulsions, so at this stage it is still not suitable for sale as a sobering-up pill. Claims have also been made that various herbal mixtures will increase the rate of alcohol elimination. In order to do this they need to react directly with the alcohol or increase the activity or concentration of the liver enzyme alcohol dehydrogenase.

In all probability someone will eventually invent a potion which is really effective but those introduced so far have been heralded with advertiser's trumpets and disappeared without trace very quickly. It should be pointed out that none of these commercial preparations has been designed in an attempt to confuse either the breath or blood tests. Their purpose, however ineffectual, is to prevent alcohol from entering the blood stream, either by absorbing it or by using it up in some other chemical process. Any attempt to market a pill deliberately designed to confuse the tests could be construed as an attempt to obstruct the law.

The biochemical processes involving alcohol in human beings are very complex but it can be said without doubt that alcohol slows reaction time, lessens co-ordination, diminishes peripheral vision and reduces tolerance to glare. Hardened drinkers are a danger to themselves, a threat to their families and a menace to those they meet.

Chapter 3

ACCIDENTS ON THE ROAD

"Drink not the third glass – which thou canst not tame When once it is within thee."

George Herbert

The fact that, on average, every day roughly sixty thousand people are killed and injured in traffic accidents throughout the world passes virtually unnoticed. The annual death toll in many countries receives little comment despite the fact that a high proportion of these deaths are directly alcohol related.

If a tragedy occurred in the USA in which over 90 people were killed it would make international headlines and be reported on every television channel in the world. If ten people were killed in Great Britain as a result of, say, a single train accident, there would doubtless be demands for a public enquiry and questions would be asked in the House of Commons. Yet that is the magnitude of the problem of road deaths in the two countries every day but, apart from the publication of normal road accident statistics and the activities of road safety organisations, most people just accept the figures and take the road casualties for granted. To put them into stark reality, in the USA three million people have been killed in road accidents since 1900 and it is known that the biggest single factor in a large proportion of those accidents has been alcohol[1].

To be involved in any form of accident is a traumatic experience both for the victims and for relatives and bystanders. It is because of the pain, agony and costs of road accidents that so much time and effort is devoted to road safety campaigns in order to eliminate sources of danger and to reduce the human element to a minimum. Nobody conscious of the enormous toll on the roads can accept the blasé attitude that 'accidents will happen'.

The cost to society of traffic accidents is enormous. It has been estimated that in the USA in 1988 the combined expense of damage, insurance, hospital treatment and lost production amounted to $74 billion. In Great Britain each fatal accident in 1993 was estimated to have cost over £860,000 and each slight injury accident cost £10,000.

Accidents rarely arise from just one single cause. In most cases a number of contributing factors apply, whether the accident is at home, in the office, on the factory floor or on the road. Poor lighting, coupled with a slippery floor and an unbuttoned overall, may lead to workers falling and catching their clothing on a handle or moving machinery. Similarly, poor street lighting and a child rushing across the road may mean another road casualty if the motorist's reactions have been slowed down by drinking alcohol or taking drugs.

The human element

Unfortunately, improvements in the design of equipment, machinery and vehicles cannot totally remove the human element which contributes so much to many accidents. This is despite the admirable criteria established by such bodies as the American Standards Association and the British Standards Institution, all aimed at improving safety in every area of design and activity. The European Union has been equally active in standardising features of motor vehicle design to improve safety for road users but so far has failed to deal fully with the variations in the national laws on drinking and driving which exist within the EU.

However, even if all external factors are dealt with and improvements made to street lighting, road surfaces repaired and annual checks carried out on cars, there remains the clear unquestionable fact that a very large proportion of accidents on the road involve drivers, cyclists and pedestrians who have alcohol in their blood.

Despite this, many people say that they drive a car better and more carefully after they have had a couple of drinks. It may be true that they drive more slowly and considerately knowing they have been drinking and aware of the penalties that could arise if they are stopped for any reason by the police. However, at least one survey has shown that the most common violation committed by drivers who have been drinking is that of driving too fast for the road conditions pertaining at that time. The simple fact of the matter is that the presence of even a small quantity of alcohol in their blood means that their ability to respond to an accident situation, whether of their own making or someone else's, is adversely affected.

Reaction times

This aspect of the physiological action of alcohol has been studied for many years in all major countries and shows that the more alcohol there is in the blood the longer it takes to react to an emergency. The slowing down of reaction time can even be measured with simple tests such as stacking children's building blocks or putting shapes through corresponding holes; but when the required reaction is one of applying a foot brake in a car, the extra few hundredths of a second taken by the drinking driver can make the difference between having an accident and avoiding one or between missing a person or killing them. Drinking motorists delude themselves into believing that it will never happen to them when the reality of the situation is that it can happen to anyone but is less likely to happen if the driver is sober.

Although laws against drunken driving were enacted soon after motor vehicles became common throughout the world, the introduction of the taking of blood samples for analysis did not occur until first introduced by Norway in 1927, followed by Sweden in 1934. The first legal limit, of 50 mg of blood, then followed in Norway in 1936 but, in Sweden, in the absence of a specific legal limit it was found that drivers with high blood alcohol levels were often freed by the municipal courts. After much debate a legal limit of 150 mg was introduced in 1941. Even at that level the figure was a generous compromise which met with considerable criticism in the country, although a less serious drink-drive offence level between 80 mg and 150 mg was introduced at the same time.

It was, however, a commonly held view in many countries that alcohol was only a major factor in less than 5% of road accidents and for this reason prosecutions were frequently only made when drivers were clearly drunk and incapable; it is now accepted that results from clinical examination for drunkenness are unreliable[2] when blood alcohol levels are below 200 mg.

It was not fully appreciated for a long time that even relatively low blood alcohol levels could lead to impairment of driving ability. Serious doubts were not cast on the 5% involvement figure until 1938 when a special comparative study on drivers was carried out in Illinois, USA[3]. In this pioneering investigation, the blood alcohol levels of drivers involved in accidents were compared with a random selection of non-accident drivers. The results showed that the higher the blood alcohol level, the greater the likelihood of being in the accident group; it also showed that 47% of the accident group had been drinking.

This work was followed by similar studies in other countries. Thus an investigation in Perth, Australia[4] in 1957 found that of 218 fatal road accident victims, 86 (39%) had blood alcohol levels exceeding 100 mg. Another study in Ontario, Canada[5] in 1959 showed that the average number of accidents per year and per 10,000 miles was far greater for drinking drivers than it was for non-drinking drivers. A more significant study in the same year[6] in the USA showed that 69% of motorists killed in accidents involving no other vehicle or person had blood alcohol levels exceeding 50 mg. Other studies in Britain[7] indicated that up to 20% of drivers killed in road accidents had been drinking and that for accidents occurring between 10.00 p.m. and 4.00 a.m. the figure was 60%. Similarly, a very careful and conservative assessment of all available data in the USA prior to 1974 showed that alcohol may have been involved in 36% of motor vehicle deaths.

Accident potential

The cumulative evidence of such results suggested a significant relationship between the blood alcohol level and the possibility of having an accident. The Illinois study in 1938 indicated that a driver with a blood alcohol level of 110 mg was 17 times more likely to be involved in an accident than under normal circumstances. A more detailed assessment carried out in 1960 in Czechoslovakia[8] produced the following relationships between the accident potential and blood alcohol:

Blood alcohol level	Accident potential
30 mg/100 mL	Taken as unity
100 mg/100 mL	7 times
150 mg/100 mL	30 times

The implication from these results and others like them was quite clear and led ultimately to a special investigation extending over 12 months in Grand Rapids, Michigan, USA. This study, directed by Professor R F Borkenstein of Indiana University[9] is such a milestone in the annals of alcohol and road accidents that it is worth considering in some detail.

Of the many human factors that could possibly relate to road accidents, it was decided to investigate the role of nine: age, education, race, marital status, sex, occupation, annual mileage driven, blood alcohol level and frequency of drinking alcohol. During the study, 5985 drivers involved in accidents were interviewed and compared with another 7590 non-accident drivers. At all times every effort was made to establish identical sampling conditions for the two groups that were studied. The results of the survey showed that young and elderly males had above average accident rates, as did poorly educated and unmarried people. It was also found that non-whites were more accident prone than were whites, as were unskilled workers as compared with skilled workers. But of greatest significance from the results was the relationship between blood alcohol levels and the possibility of having an accident. Despite the fact that in the years since the study was carried out differing interpretations have been made on some of the data, the results show quite conclusively that as the blood alcohol level rises so does the likelihood of having an accident.

A much more recent study has been carried out in Germany[10], repeating the experimental protocol employed in the Grand Rapids Survey. The reliability of the previous work, carried out thirty years earlier, was clearly demonstrated by results which produced an almost identical curve for the relationship between blood alcohol levels and the risk of having an accident.

The British Medical Association summarised the various drinking-driving results in *The Drinking Driver* in 1965 when they pointed out that at the 60 mg level the accident potential was doubled, at the 100 mg level it was increased sixfold and at the 150 mg level the likelihood of being involved in an accident was increased twenty-five times (similar figures have also been presented by Professor Borkenstein[11]). When plotted on a graph these values produce a smooth curve which shows that any increase in accident potential is slight until the 50 mg level has been attained (this corresponds to about 22 µg for the breath alcohol level). It is now accepted that the increase in accident potential does vary, depending upon the age and experience of the drinking driver, as shown in Figure 8. However, it is quite clear from a consideration of the risk of having an accident that blood alcohol levels as high as 80 mg (the legally accepted level in Great Britain and a number of other European countries) cannot be considered 'safe' and drivers attaining such figures are more likely to be involved in traffic accidents than they would be if their blood alcohol level were below the 50 mg level.

Although these figures relate to road accidents, the fact that response tests, simulators and eye tests *all* demonstrate impairment or undesirable changes due to alcohol implies that it is not just road accidents in which alcohol plays a part. The presence of alcohol in the blood increases the possibility of an accident or an error in any situation involving machinery or precision working. Clearly, evidence has now been obtained to show that impairment by alcohol is also a major factor in accidents occurring in transportation in general, especially in aviation and railways[12]. It is believed that in the USA 10% of fatal aviation accidents involve alcohol and it may be a factor in as many as 70% of fatal boating accidents.

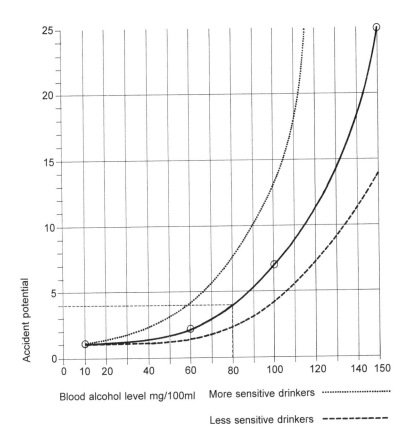

Figure 8 – Relationship between blood alcohol level and the likelihood of having an accident.

Accident peaks

In the case of road accidents, the peak period for alcohol related deaths occurs after heavy drinking sessions at the end of the week. In Great Britain, about 50% of drink-drive fatalities occur between 10.00 p.m. and 4.00 a.m. on Friday, Saturday and Sunday nights and similar maximum accident periods exist in other countries. It should, however, be pointed out that the majority of people *do not* combine drinking and driving. This fact was clearly shown by the Borkenstein survey and was reinforced some years later by a study in Canberra,

Australia[13], in which it was shown that 80% of driving was done in the absence of alcohol. Even between 10.00 p.m. and 2.00 a.m., 75% of tested drivers had no alcohol in their blood. Similar studies in Sweden[14] indicated that up to 92% of motorists studied had not driven while under the influence of alcohol during a twelve month period. What these studies confirm is that a totally disproportionate number of road accidents and deaths are caused by a very small number of anti-social motorists. The majority of drinking/driving is probably done by an anti-social, self-centred group comprising less than 5% of all motorists[15].

As a result of cumulative evidence from all over the world, a major reassessment had to be made concerning the relationship between alcohol and road accidents. *All* studies showed that it was a major factor in a substantial proportion of road accidents and even superficial investigations clearly demonstrated that a large number of motorists killed in accidents had been drinking heavily.

Although breath tests, mainly for roadside screening purposes, had been introduced before World War II in parts of the USA, the more general introduction throughout the developed countries of the world did not occur until the 1950s and 1960s. To begin with, most countries relied on various forms of the tube and bag as a means of roadside testing, backed up by blood or urine sampling at the police station. During the 1970s there was a great improvement in the quality of the instruments available both for roadside screening and for evidential testing with the result that, in most places, the tube and bag at the roadside has given way to electronic screening devices and the chemical analysis of blood and urine samples has been replaced by either gas chromatographic analysis or by evidential breath testing.

Compared with the USA and the Scandinavian countries, Great Britain was slow in introducing even the roadside screening of motorists and it was not until October 1967 that the dreaded 'breath test law' came into force. Prior to the commencement of these tests, it had been cautiously estimated by the Royal Society for the Prevention of Accidents (RoSPA) that a reduction of about 5% in the number of road casualties could be expected following the new law.

In the event the initial results obtained were dramatic, with a reduction of 11% in road casualties being achieved during the first 12 months. During the 12 months prior to the breath tests, there were 7920 fatalities on the roads in Great Britain and in the subsequent three years the corresponding figures were 6732, 7087 and 7424, despite the fact that during the same time there was a continual increase in the number of vehicles on the roads. Similar types of reductions in road casualties were also experienced in Canada, New Zealand and the Australian states when this type of breath test law was introduced. However, in almost every case the results of the introduction of the tests followed a similar pattern in that the initial period showing a substantial reduction in road casualties was followed by a gradual falling-off of the deterrent effect. In fact, in Great Britain by the end of 1973, road casualties had reached virtually the same level as they had been prior to October 1967.

What was equally important was that by 1976 the proportion of motorists and motorcyclists killed whose blood alcohol levels exceeded the legal limit of 80 mg/100 mL had reached 38%, compared with the pre-1967 figure of 32%. However, it should be emphasised that there was a corresponding upward trend in the amount of traffic on the roads during much of this period. In practice, the fall-off rate in Great Britain was much less than that in Canada, where road casualty figures returned to their original level within about 12 months following the introduction of the Federal 80 mg limit, and France where the deterrent effect of their 1978 law appeared to disappear within a matter of a few months due to the lack of police enthusiasm.

A variety of reasons have been given for this early decline in the effect of the law. It is certain that people initially become ultra-cautious after new controls of this type are passed until they are able to assess how much effort the police will put into

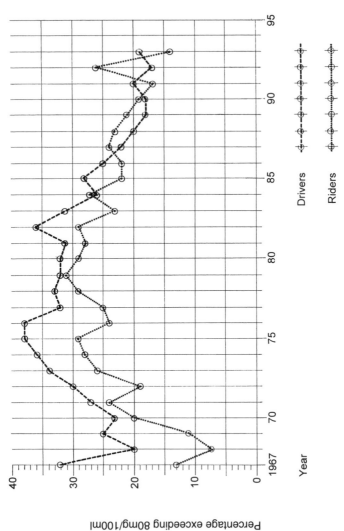

Figure 9 – Proportion of drivers and motorcyclists killed in road accidents in Great Britain with blood alcohol levels exceeding the legal limit of 80 mg/100 mL.

enforcing the regulations. When they find that the actual possibility of being stopped is quite small, they start to disregard the law. In addition to this, every year brings newly qualified drivers on to the roads who have not been subjected to the original propaganda and pressures when the law was first introduced. This means that to maintain the momentum it is necessary to have regular drink-drive safety campaigns backed up by guidance and education schemes. Fortunately, subsequent campaigns and strengthened legislation have led to total road deaths in Great Britain being halved and alcohol related deaths being reduced to roughly one-third of what they were.

Ways in which any fall-off can be prevented in the future include the introduction of additional stricter laws, such as lowering the legal blood alcohol level further (Sweden reached its present 20 mg level in four stages) and by lectures and special guidance to teenagers at schools before they become drinkers or drivers. The old adage that 'prevention is better than cure' is of considerable importance in the areas concerning alcohol and drugs.

The most recent successes of drink-drive laws in Australia have been achieved by greatly increasing the probability of all motorists being stopped and tested using mobile evidential test centres, coupled with a legal limit of 50 mg/100 mL. Random breath testing means that in New South Wales there is a 1 in 3 chance of a motorist being stopped and tested in any one year compared with roughly a 1 in 40 chance of being breath tested at the roadside in Great Britain. Despite this, the consistent pressure for road safety campaigns, coupled with other safety measures, has led to the proportion of drivers and motorcyclists over the legal limit dropping to below 20% of all fatalities (Figure 9).

Campaigns against drink-driving have been greatly assisted by increased support from brewers and publicans being prepared to support the display of posters and safety publicity material in public houses and bars. However, it is still questionable whether or not the installation of self-testing machines is of any great help. The results from such machines have no legal validity and may be misleading if the test is carried out soon after drinking, as it may be artificially high due to a 'mouth alcohol effect' (see page 103) or artificially low if alcohol is still passing into the blood stream.

One of the strongest blocks to getting motorists to appreciate the importance of not combining drinking and driving has been the way in which the public at large have tended to take the attitude 'there but for the grace of God go I' and have regarded drinking drivers as being unlucky if they get caught. There is, in fact, not enough social stigma to being labelled a drinking driver. There has been an almost total failure to face the fact that the drinker is a real danger and menace to life once behind the wheel of a car or on a motorcycle. Road safety campaigns need to be directed as much at the non-drinkers as at the drinkers – possibly along the lines of 'Don't go in a car with a drinking driver' or 'My Dad and Mum don't drink and drive!'

An international problem

It should be remembered that the incidence of alcohol-related accidents is not limited to any particular country or area or even to one type of road user. Extreme difficulties do, however, exist in making direct comparisons between the accident figures of one country and those of another so that 'league tables' expressed in terms of casualties per 1000 vehicles or per 10,000 population must be treated with caution. Such comparisons do not allow for population densities, variations in hours of daylight, weather conditions or miles of motorways, freeways and dual carriageways. Any relationship between those who are killed in road accidents and their blood alcohol levels has to be limited to those casualties who die within six hours of the traffic accident occurring[16]. If the victim survives longer than this it is very likely that the alcohol has been broken down in the body in any case. In addition to this, not all countries have adopted the United Nations Economic Commission for Europe recommendation for road casualties in which the classifications made are:

Deaths: people reported killed if death occurs within thirty days of the accident.

Serious injury: where a person is detained as an in-patient in hospital, or has suffered from a well-defined injury requiring medical treatment.

Slight injury: an injury of a minor nature like a bruise or sprain. Shock is not included under this heading unless medical treatment has been required.

However, even with guidance over casualty classification, comparisons are still difficult as checks for the presence of alcohol are not always carried out following road accidents, especially in developing countries and some nations which are major wine producers are loath to draw attention to the accident involvement of their most important industry.

Age and drink

What accident statistics do reveal very clearly is a disproportionate number of road casualties in the younger age groups. This, again, is a common feature in all developed countries in which teenagers have access to motorcycles and cars. In Victoria, Australia, the 18–26 age group was considered to be the core of the drink-drive problem[17] and this was reinforced by figures from Queensland[18] showing that 25% of motorcyclists killed had more than 100 mg/100 mL of blood alcohol. Similar figures from the USA showed[19] that about half of all traffic fatalities in that country occurred with people under the age of 25 years and that drivers between the ages of 16 and 24 years accounted for nearly 50% of all alcohol related single vehicle crashes leading to the driver's death. A similar survey[20] carried out in Great Britain in 1980 showed that, of over 1000 drink-drive offences studied, nearly a quarter of the offenders were under 25 years of age, although their average blood alcohol level of 153 mg/100 mL was lower than the value for the older age groups. Other British studies[21] revealed that 20% of driver deaths (many of them motorcyclists) occurred in the 16–19 age group and nearly 40% in the 16–24 age group.

These appalling figures have led to a major targeting of road safety campaigns, drink-drive education and, in some cases, legislation towards the younger, less experienced riders and drivers. The high number of alcohol-related accidents in this section of the population can be attributed to the fact that people are able to afford motorcycles and cars at a younger age than was the case 15 or 20 years ago. So some of the increase is due to the greater mobility of teenagers and people in their early twenties. Within the USA, a great deal of effort is going into improved driver education in schools and there is every reason to emphasise the responsibilities that go with obtaining a driving licence, and the attendant dangers of drinking, whilst teenagers are still at school and before they gain the freedom of the road. There is very little hope for any improvement in the future unless some guidance is given at a much earlier stage than at present. Once a teenager has his or her 'wheels' it is often too late; by that time the physical and psychological feel of freedom means that in all too many cases caution is thrown to the winds.

Because the accident statistics clearly showed a high alcohol-related crash involvement amongst young drivers, all states in the USA have passed legislation raising the minimum age at which intoxicating liquors can be purchased to 21 years[22]. In addition to this, the problem of the young drink-driving has been tackled by introducing special low drink-drive limits. In Australia the legal limit for *all* novice drivers is only 20 mg and in states in the USA it varies with some levels being as low as zero (Arizona, D.C., Minnesota, Oregon, Utah, Washington and Wisconsin) and 20 mg (Arkansas, Maine, Maryland, New Mexico, Ohio, Tennessee, Vermont), usually for drivers under the age of 21 years.

Within Great Britain increased campaigning directed towards younger drivers has led to the percentage of drivers above the legal limit killed in the 20–29 age group dropping[23] from 42% to 28% over the ten year period 1983–1993. This has occurred at the same time as the overall number of road casualties has been reduced dramatically due to a wide range of road safety measures.

Public concern

Although governments and road safety organisations in most countries have tried to alert people to the dangers of drinking and driving, there is no doubt that it is predominantly in the USA that the general public have become not only concerned but greatly involved in trying to control the mayhem on the roads. It has been calculated that in the USA approximately 18,000 persons (50 per day) are killed annually in road accidents involving a drunken driver and more than a quarter of a million people suffer injuries. Many of the casualties are young children and teenagers and it has been because of the deaths of husbands and their offspring that women who have suffered loss due to drunken motorists have established organisations such as MADD (Mothers Against Drunk Drivers) and RID (Remove Intoxicated Drivers). These are pressure groups which set out to obtain heavier penalties against convicted drivers and seek greater action to catch the drunken motorists before they actually have accidents. The strength of public feeling is shown by the fact that MADD, started in California in 1980, grew within two years to 83 chapters (branches) in 29 states and RID, founded in New York, grew to 55 chapters in the same period of time. Within ten years, the two organisations had grown[24] to about 500 chapters and led Senator John Danforth in 1988 to say of MADD:

> "This organisation has made the public realise that drunk driving is not a victimless crime. This change in public attitude has made it possible for those of us in Congress and in state legislatures to pass stronger drunk driving laws."

These organisations have already been responsible for pressuring for the state legislation which raised the minimum age for the consumption of alcohol, increased penalties for refusing breath and blood samples and, in some cases, the suspension of the driving licence immediately after the offence. As a result of MADD campaigns, drunk driving arrests in Maryland increased by 45% and road deaths dropped by 20%. While not everyone has been in agreement with the campaign approach to stricter penalties in all cases, these organisations have made a considerable impact and brought about the public awareness that is still needed in most other countries.

It is encouraging to be able to point out that not all aspects of the driving scene are bad, the one bright spot being women drivers. Despite all the jokes and criticisms over their driving abilities, women are normally much more responsible than men. All the surveys in different countries show that women are more moderate drinkers, with about 20% being total abstainers. Women very rarely attain the high blood alcohol levels that frequently occur with men, but as more women are driving and becoming more independent, there appears to be an increase in women driving under the influence of drink. However, studies show that women generally drink less alcohol than men and as a result are involved in proportionately fewer accidents when under its influence[25]. This also applies to other offences committed under the influence of alcohol.

Pedestrians and cyclists

Legislators have been so concerned about the involvement of drinking drivers in the road accident statistics that, in their haste to deal with the problem, they have failed to consider the role of other road users. As a result, current legislation such as that in Britain does not apply to pedestrians, cyclists or horse riders. It is possible for a perfectly sober motorist to be involved in an accident caused by a drunken cyclist and for them to be required by law to give a breath sample whilst the cyclist cannot be made to give samples under any circumstances. The possibility of a miscarriage of justice occurring because of this is enormous.

The only time any evidence of alcohol consumption can be obtained against a cyclist or pedestrian is if they are killed and a blood sample is taken in the autopsy. Despite this major omission from the law, the role of pedestrians is far from insignificant, yet the comment made by B E Sabey and P J Codling as long ago as 1974 that "non-drinking drivers may suffer as a consequence of the actions of drinking pedestrians" has been totally ignored[26].

It is not unexpected to find that, since the 1967 Road Safety Act in Britain did not apply to pedestrians, blood alcohol figures for those killed in traffic accidents were, and still are, virtually unaffected[27]. A study carried out soon after the Act came into force showed that one-third of pedestrians killed had been drinking and 21% had levels exceeding 80 mg. By 1992 this figure had increased to 33% and appeared to be on a rising trend, although the number of actual casualties fell over the 25 year period.

These figures are significantly greater than for pedestrians not involved in accidents and indicate that alcohol is once again an important factor to be considered. This is particularly so at night time when 70% of those killed in accidents had blood alcohol levels exceeding 80 mg. It is also an area in which males predominate over females[28].

Although detailed studies on pedestrians are less common than those on motorists, there is nothing exceptional in the British figures, as one study carried out in Australia found that 38% of injured pedestrians (over the age of 14) had been drinking[29], and another in North Carolina, USA, showed that 50% of dead pedestrians had some alcohol in their blood and 8% had drugs[30].

A very detailed study of pedestrian involvement in accidents in New Orleans[31] showed that 50% of fatal and non-fatal adult pedestrians had been drinking and of these about half had blood alcohol levels exceeding 200 mg. Accidents involving the drinking pedestrian tended to occur at night and at weekends, a similar pattern to that for drinking motorists.

Despite the very clear involvement of alcohol in pedestrian-related road accidents, all countries seem loath to impose some form of breath or blood sampling, even when it is medically acceptable. However, the log jam on this may well have been broken by New South Wales, Australia, imposing compulsory blood testing on *all* road users hospitalised following traffic accidents.

Of all the accident figures, those for cyclists vary the greatest from one year to the next. In Britain, this variation depends greatly upon weather conditions and the popularity of cycling itself, which in turn depends upon petrol prices, the cost of public transport and campaigns to encourage physical exercise. On average only about 10% of cyclists over the age of 16 killed have alcohol levels exceeding 80 mg. One major reason for this is that the age distribution for cyclists involved in accidents is not representative of the population as a whole. Alcohol-related accidents with cyclists tend to be much greater in those countries in which bicycles are a common means of transport. In Münster, Germany, where almost everyone has a bicycle, a study[32] of cyclist fatalities over a period of five years showed 31.3% had blood alcohol levels exceeding 20 mg.

Whichever way such statistics are considered it is quite clear that all drinking road users are involved in a totally disproportionate number of road accidents and the failure to include pedestrians and cyclists in breath and blood testing legislation is a case of turning a blind eye to the realities of the situation. At the very least, there is every justification for requiring those cyclists and pedestrians involved in accidents to provide breath and blood samples on equal terms to those applicable to motorists and motorcyclists[33].

Deterrent

Very large sums of money are now being spent by various traffic authorities around the world in efforts to deter the drinking driver. However, the strongest deterrent of all appears to come from the potential loss of the right to drive following very determined efforts by police to apprehend the drinking motorist. It has been claimed that vigorous law enforcement with road blocks and random testing, as in Australia and Scandinavia, does have a significant effect. However, this is only of limited success if the banned driver still continues to drive after being sentenced. There is a great need for the names and addresses of convicted motorists (and all criminals) to be published in local newspapers where they reside and to encourage greater involvement of the general public in informing the police of suspected drinking drivers. The use of rehabilitation centres and alcohol education for repeat offenders and those with very high blood alcohol levels is becoming more common in an effort to try and break the circle of cause and effect for the most problematic group of drivers. Coupled with this is an increasing use of breath controlled inter-lock[34] devices, in Canada, Australia and the USA, which will only permit drivers to start their cars if their breath alcohol levels are below 20–30 mg.

However, the one thing that appears to deter all the time is the chance of being caught and at present, despite all police efforts, that likelihood is, in many countries, still too small.

Chapter 4

WHICH LEGAL LIMIT?

*"Woe unto them that rise up early in the
morning, that they may follow strong drink; that
continue until night, till wine enflame them."*

Isaiah ch. 5, v.11

One of the major problems that has confronted legislators
throughout the world has been that of deciding what the legal
limit should be. This has been made even more difficult with
the advent of evidential breath testing, as legislators have been
placed in the position of having to decide whether to convert
breath alcohol values to the corresponding blood alcohol level
(and run into the problems of appropriate conversion factors)
or to introduce a legal breath alcohol limit. That there is no
international consensus of opinion on this is clear, as the
variation is from no legal limit at one end, through high levels
of 150 mg, to absolute zero in a few instances.

The situation is even more confusing for the international
traveller who usually has no idea of the wide variations which
exist from one country to another. As a result, it is easy to
infringe the laws unwittingly when visiting a foreign country
unless special efforts are made to ascertain what the drink-
drive rules may be.

From the shape of the curve in Figure 8 (page 53), it can be
seen that the possibility of having an accident increases
dramatically at high blood alcohol levels. The problem facing
legislators is obviously one of deciding at which point the limit
is chosen to achieve the maximum deterrent effect. Too high
an accepted level will mean a large proportion of highly
accident prone people still being allowed to drive and too low
a level could lead to the courts becoming overloaded with
drink-drive cases, many of which were of no significant danger.
The level selected should be one that acts as a definite
deterrent, is not high enough for the motorist to be a

significantly greater risk than normal and is a level for which
the majority of the public will have respect and consider
reasonable. It has been stated that the level should not be one
that would interfere with the normal practice of the 'social
drinker'. But such statements beg the question and require a
definition of what is a social drinker. At the same time, today's
social drinker may become next year's alcoholic and it is clear
that the first objective should be to reduce the number of road
accidents by gaining the maximum support and co-operation
from the public. In the USA, which is very much a car-
orientated society, the tendency has been to apply legal limits
which really only restrict the more problematic and heavy
drinkers. Inevitably, the final legislated figure is likely to be a
compromise but it should not be based upon the vague
concept of not interfering with the drinking habits of the
'social drinker'.

What limit?

The ideal solution is to specify that there should be no alcohol
in the blood at all – in other words the law should be "Don't
drink before you drive". However, this is virtually impossible
to operate legally because of the fact that a low level of alcohol
seems to persist in the blood in any case[1]. For this reason, even
those countries with zero limits rarely take action in practice
if the blood level is found to be below 30 mg. An alternative
approach to the problem is to assess at which point the chance
of a person having an accident is likely to start increasing and
to use this as the legal limit that should not be exceeded.

The very considerable differences that do exist between the
legal breath and blood alcohol limits of various nations owe
much to the different interpretations put upon the available
statistical and physiological data, but these are not arbitrary
figures just plucked from the air. As will have been seen
already in Chapter 3 and from the work and conferences of
the International Council on Alcohol, Drugs and Traffic
Safety, there is total acceptance of the relationship between
alcohol and accidents. Over the years this has led to the
accumulation of considerable data on the responses of people

after drinking alcoholic beverages. Every conceivable form of test has been carried out to investigate co-ordination and reaction times in people who have consumed different quantities of alcohol under various conditions. Tests employed have ranged from simple finger to finger touching exercises to the more involved use of construction sets, written examinations and complex traffic simulators. Even the most elementary of these tests have given results that support the general conclusions that the greater the level of blood alcohol, the slower the speed of reaction to an emergency.

Deterioration of actions

It is accepted by the medical profession that the effect of alcohol leads to a progressive deterioration of co-ordination. The idea that a very small quantity of alcohol can lead to an improvement in a driver's response has been discredited as measurable deterioration has been observed in subjects with only a 10 mg blood alcohol level. Many years ago Dr Hebbelinck[2] showed that people with blood alcohol levels as low as 30 mg exhibited greatly decreased posture control and a reduction in physical power, indicating that any alcohol taken prior to competitive sport is likely to be detrimental to the performance.

It has been claimed that measurable deterioration of driving skills actually occurs with some subjects as soon as any alcohol enters the blood stream[3]. Certainly, reduced visual activity[4] and deterioration of performance on driving simulators has been clearly demonstrated[5] at levels of 20–30 mg. One particular series of tests[6], carried out with trade union co-operation, clearly illustrated the dangers of even low blood alcohol levels. Manchester (England) Corporation busmen were given whisky to drink and then asked to drive their buses through various gaps between poles. The results showed that in most cases the alcohol encouraged them to go through narrower gaps than normal. In one instance, an experienced driver tried to drive the 8 ft (2.44 m) wide bus through a gap of 6 ft 8 ins (2.03 m); his blood alcohol level was only 26 mg. The general conclusion reached from the study was that even blood alcohol levels below 50 mg cannot be considered absolutely safe.

Similar studies in other countries substantiate the view that at no stage does alcohol lead to an improvement in driving ability or general self-control. Contrary to popular belief, the reaction time and co-ordination tests do not reveal any great variation between different people, be they abstainers or hardened drinkers, although the latter group is probably better at hiding the effects of drinking when it comes to talking and general demeanour.

The 50 mg level

Although the legal blood alcohol limits applied in most countries have been set quite high, it has been generally accepted for many years that impairment of responses and abilities actually occurs at the very low levels already mentioned. As early as 1938, the National Safety Council in the USA felt that it was only when the blood alcohol level was less than 50 mg that it was possible to say that a driver's ability was not impaired to the point of making him dangerous. It was, however, not until 1957 that a more specific recommendation[7] was made that a 50 mg limit should apply, although few states took any notice of the suggestion at the time. Even now[8], it is considered encouraging that drivers in the USA are responding to the 100 mg level!

As long ago as 1960, a special committee of the British Medical Association produced a report[9] which, among its conclusions, said:

> "*The Committee considers that a concentration of 50 mg of alcohol in 100 ml of blood while driving a motor vehicle is the highest that can be accepted as entirely consistent with the safety of other road users.** While there may be circumstances in which individual driving ability will not depreciate significantly by the time this level is reached, the Committee is impressed by the rapidity with which deterioration occurs at blood levels in excess of 100 mg/100 mL. This is true even in the case of hardened

---

* Author's italics

drinkers and experienced drivers. The Committee cannot conceive of any circumstances in which it could be considered safe for a person to drive a motor vehicle on the public roads with an amount of alcohol in the blood greater than 150 mg/ 100 mL."

Similarly, a 1962 report in Canada[10] stated quite unambiguously:

"Since impairment of driving ability occurs in some drivers at a blood alcohol level of 0.05 per cent (50 mg/100 mL), this is the highest level that can be accepted as consistent with highway safety."

Up to the 50 mg level, impairment of co-ordination, whilst measurable by response tests, is unlikely to be noticeable to the casual observer. Above this level, progressive impairment is noticeable even without resorting to tests and is the reason the 50 mg level is accepted by some countries as being the starting point for prosecution. The operator handbook for the Intoximeter 3000 evidential breath testing machine used extensively throughout the world states very clearly[11] that a breath alcohol value above 15 µg/100 mL (blood 35 mg/100 mL) produces symptoms of "increased self-confidence and decreased inhibitions. Loss of attention, judgement and control by decrease in co-ordination and perception."

Above 100 mg, deterioration of response to the various co-ordination tests occurs rapidly and is the reason that this level has been accepted as suitable for prosecution by rather more liberal legislators. It is difficult to understand how any legislative body concerned with reducing the number of road accidents can justify the use of the 150 mg level as a minimum to warrant prosecution. The various response tests show that between the 100 and 150 mg levels impairment is so serious that any driver with this amount of alcohol in his system is highly accident-prone.

After reading all the investigations, reports and analyses it is difficult to understand why it has taken some countries so long to apply any legal limit at all and why any level in excess of 50

mg has been considered as an acceptable risk. The evidence
shows quite clearly that once the 50 mg level is reached there
is a significant increase in the possibility of having an accident.
It is not simply a case of the driver not being able to drive
correctly but the fact that his or her ability to respond to an
accident situation has been impaired that is important. It is
not a valid argument to accept levels up to 80 mg–100 mg just
on the basis that these are levels attained by social drinkers
whilst the higher levels are associated with problem drinkers[12].
The real intention should be to deter any drinker from adding
to the road accident figures, whether that person is a social
drinker or an alcoholic. In practice, the amount of alcohol that
has to be drunk in a short space of time to attain an 80 mg level
is quite substantial, as is obvious from the calculations using
the Widmark formula on page 41. After allowing for normal
drinking time and delays for driving, arresting and evidential
testing, it is quite obvious that a normal 'social' drinker is
unlikely to reach an 80 mg level. These factors alone show that
the operative limit in most cases is about 30 mg above the legal
limit[13]. This means that in Great Britain a driver has to be
above the 100 mg level when first stopped by the police to
stand a real chance of being successfully prosecuted for a
drink-drive offence as the tolerances and allowances in the law
are all expressed to the driver's advantage.

It is only fair to point out that in recent years attitudes towards
the drinking driver have started to change, along with a
greater appreciation that the problem drinker is someone
who requires medical attention if he or she is to be cured. As
a result of this, there is a general trend to lower legal drink-
drive limits, more positive law enforcement and attempts at
special guidance for second and third offenders in some
countries. At the same time, drinking and driving is being
treated as a more serious offence that it was 20 or 30 years ago.

Legal limits

All countries appear to approach the introduction of legal
blood alcohol limits with a certain degree of trepidation and
it was almost certainly the concern about adverse public

reaction that led to levels as high as 150 mg being initially introduced in Sweden and later in some states in the USA. In Great Britain, the possibility of using body fluids for alcohol analysis was first incorporated into the Road Traffic Act 1962 but no legal limits were specified. This part of the law was ignored until the 80 mg limit was later introduced following the Road Safety Act 1967. Great Britain then joined what was at the time a small group of countries which had compromised between the more scientifically valid level of 50 mg and the highly liberal level of 100 mg. In recent years, as accidents have continued to occur and research has become even more conclusive, other countries have lowered their limits to 80 mg or even to below 50 mg. No arguments have been forthcoming to increase the legally accepted blood alcohol levels and there is every evidence that ultimately the trend will be to an almost uniform 50 mg figure as distinct from the 80 mg now more common in Europe. The only case in which a legal blood alcohol level has been increased occurred when East and West Germany were re-united. The two former separate governments agreed on a compromise level of 50 mg in place of the 0 mg in East Germany and 80 mg in West Germany. Other than this, the international trend has been steadily downwards. The levels currently applicable throughout much of the world are listed in Table 5 on page 75.

The law on drinking and driving in Northern Ireland, introduced in 1968, differed fairly substantially from that in the rest of the UK. Even at that time, the law classified blood alcohol levels exceeding 125 mg as constituting a more serious offence and from an early date used evidential breath testing machines, the 'Breathalyzer' and 'Alcolmeter', in place of the more common blood analysis. The use of sophisticated equipment of this type put Northern Ireland well ahead of most countries in its efforts to control the drinking driver.

In the 50 states of the USA, the situation is inevitably rather confusing as they are each responsible for their own legislation. Although levels have differed considerably from one state to another, there is extensive use of advanced forms of breath testing and a general willingness to consider new approaches which is refreshing when compared with other countries. As a result, the majority of states have moved towards a general 100 mg (0.10%) limit with many imposing tighter restrictions on young drivers. Strong pressures now exist to reduce the levels uniformly to 80 mg (0.08%).

As with traffic lights and speed restrictions, the breath test and blood alcohol limits are added infringements upon peoples' rights and freedoms. They have, however, only been imposed in the interests of the community as a whole. One's rights and freedoms only extend so far as they do not interfere with the corresponding rights of others. To enjoy the privilege of driving a piece of machinery weighing a few hundred kilograms at high speed along the roads, we must be prepared to forego the right to imbibe simultaneously a large quantity of alcoholic liquor. As is frequently the case, this type of law has to be imposed because of the irresponsible and anti-social behaviour of a minority of the population.

Types of tests

It is very important for the motorist to appreciate the difference between a roadside breath alcohol screening test and the later breath or blood sampling at the police station. The screening test is simply a process whereby the police can ascertain whether or not a person has an amount of alcohol in his system that is near to or above the legal maximum selected by the country concerned. The results on these devices do not usually serve as a basis for prosecution for being over the legal limit. It is the later evidential test on breath, blood, urine or saliva (in some cases) which establishes whether or not the legal limit has been exceeded and upon which a motorist can be prosecuted. However, procedures differ greatly from one country to another and, in some, the use of mobile test vans enables evidential results to be obtained at the roadside, cutting out the beneficial delays which occur for motorists if they are taken to a police station for processing.

Although most studies have been carried out with motorists in mind, the observations on impairment of response and co-ordination apply equally to users of other means of transport and machinery. The heavy drinker is just as much a danger on a bicycle, directing a crane or piloting a motor boat as he is driving a car.

Table 5

International Blood Alcohol Limits

0 mg	Bulgaria, Czech Republic, Hungary, Saudi Arabia, Slovak Republic.
20 mg	Poland, Sweden (breath 10 μg).
30 mg	India.
50 mg	Australia (young drivers 20 mg), Belgium (breath 25 μg), Finland, France, Germany, Iceland, Japan, Monaco, Netherlands (breath 22 μg), Norway, Portugal, Turkey (commercial drivers 0 mg).
80 mg	Austria (breath 40 μg), Canada, Denmark, Guernsey C.I. (breath 35 μg), Great Britain (breath 35 μg), Greece, Ireland, Italy, Jersey C.I. (breath 35 μg), Luxembourg, New Zealand (breath 40 μg, young drivers 30 mg), Northern Ireland (more severe penalty over 125 mg), South Africa, Spain, Switzerland, *USA (11 states).
100 mg	Puerto Rico, Romania, *USA (39 states and D.C.).
No legal limit	Malta (150 mg in practice).

This information has been collated from a variety of sources but, as levels are frequently being changed, *no guarantee* can be given concerning a particular value and the international traveller is advised to check the law in any country or state prior to travelling.

* All US states operate implied consent laws (see page 120) and prohibit the operation of a motor vehicle while the driver is under the influence of intoxicating liquor. Many operate lower drink-drive limits for young drivers ranging from 0 mg to 60 mg. *All* US states operate a limit of 40 mg for commercial drivers.

Chapter 5

ROADSIDE BREATH TESTS

"You must stir it and stump it,
And blow your own trumpet,
Or trust me you haven't a chance."

W S Gilbert

The progressive development of drink-drive legislation in most countries, usually over many years, has led to a variety of testing procedures evolving. However, there are usually two distinct stages in the process. The first stage is the screening test, commonly carried out at the roadside; and the second stage is the evidential test (also called the substantive test), most frequently carried out at the police station. Countries and states using mobile 'booze buses' usually dispense with a screening test as they can apply an 'on-the-spot' evidential test.

The early development of instruments for testing breath alcohol levels started in the USA as long ago as 1927, soon after Dr E Bogen[1] demonstrated that breath samples could give a reliable guide to the corresponding blood alcohol levels. This 'first generation' equipment relied heavily upon chemical reactions, usually carried out in aqueous solutions. Although the devices were used primarily for screening purposes at the roadside, some were also intended to provide fairly accurate blood alcohol values (based upon analysis of the breath alcohol level) for evidential purposes to be used in prosecutions.

The first practical roadside breath test instrument was called the 'Drunkometer' and was introduced[2] in the USA in 1938. The breath sample was collected direct into a balloon and then was pumped through a solution of acidified potassium permanganate. A similar device named the 'Intoximeter' was introduced in 1941 but this was more portable and only used for screening purposes[3,4]. It bore no relationship to the much more technically advanced Intoximeters currently used for evidential breath testing. An entirely different wet chemical

77

process involving the use of iodine vapour to produce a blue colour with starch and potassium iodide was employed in the 'Alcometer' (*not* to be confused with the later Alcolmeter). This was an evidential breath testing instrument and was the first instrument to employ a photoelectric detector for this purpose[5]. It tended, however, to be used rather more for screening purposes than for its conclusive analytical results[6].

The early breath testing devices were all based upon chemical reactions between alcohol and a coloured reagent which was either destroyed or changed (see Appendix). This created problems for the police as they had to carry around strongly acidic and corrosive solutions. Spillages of the chemicals could easily occur once the tubes or bottles had been opened. For this reason it was necessary to find simple roadside screening systems requiring little or no direct handling of chemicals.

The tube and bag

The problems associated with producing roadside screening devices were studied in Germany in the early 1950s where a simple, cheap test procedure was being sought[7]. Research on different reactions led the Drägerwerk Company of Lübeck, specialists in methods of detecting small quantities of gases and vapours, to manufacture an apparatus[8,9] in which the reagents were impregnated on a solid support and retained in a sealed glass tube. This particular apparatus was used in Germany for more than 15 years and also in Sweden and Austria before it was adopted by Great Britain in 1967. For many years it was the most well known of all breath testing equipment.

The main requirements of screening devices are that the equipment has to be portable, robust and small enough to be carried in police cars and on motorcycles. In addition, the test has to be easily applied and provide rapid results accurate enough to indicate if the subject has a breath alcohol level "clearly above the prescribed limit". For chemical tube devices it is necessary for the sealed chemicals not to deteriorate during a reasonable shelf storage period.

Breath test tubes of this type usually consist of a bright yellow-orange mixture of sulphuric acid and potassium dichromate, plus a couple of other minor components, impregnated on solid silica gel particles by heating at 100–200 °C. This produces a granular solid packing material which retains the colour of the reagent mixture. Once prepared, the 'crystals' are immediately packed and sealed in the special glass tubes, as exposure to the atmosphere can lead to a partial colour change occurring and an erroneously high reading of breath alcohol being obtained.

In Great Britain, the only screening device approved in 1967 was, in fact, the 'Alcotest 80' manufactured by Dräger Ltd. at Blyth, Northumberland. This very rapidly became known colloquially throughout Great Britain as the 'Breathalyser'. The number 80 in the name refers to the blood alcohol limit which the tube is designed to detect. Similar 'Alcotest 50' and 'Alcotest 100' tubes also exist for use in countries with other legal limits. About 15 years later, another tube and bag device, called the 'Alcolyser', manufactured by Lion Laboratories plc at Barry, Wales was also approved[10] (Figure 10 overleaf). The two tubes differ slightly in overall dimensions but operate on the same chemical principal, involving the formation of green chromium sulphate as a coloured zone in the tube in proportion to the quantity of alcohol in the breath sample blown through the tube.

There are three main parts to the equipment (Figure 11) and these have to be assembled before a screening test can be carried out. The mouthpiece (A) is of plastic and is kept in a sealed container before being used. It is designed to give a close fit when pushed onto the glass tube (B). The chemically impregnated silica gel is held in place in the tube, measuring about 3 inches (8 cm) long and 0.4 inches (1 cm) in diameter, by means of pieces of fine wire mesh.

To ensure that the tube is used the correct way round, it is marked with a blue arrow to show the direction in which the air should be blown and has a white band at the blowing end and a yellow band at the bag end. Another narrow yellow line

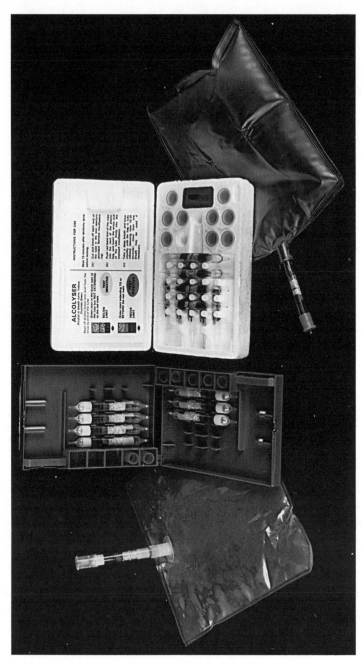

Figure 10 – Dräger Alcotest 80 and Lion Alcolyser tube and bag roadside screening devices.

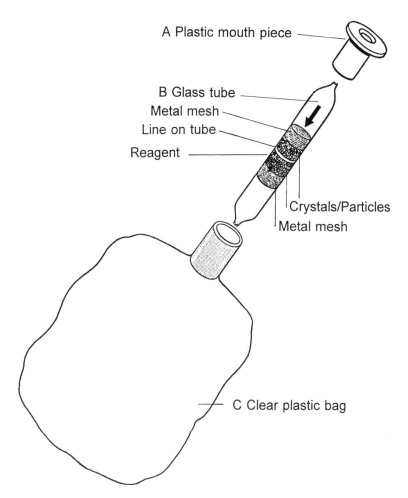

A Plastic mouth piece

B Glass tube
Metal mesh
Line on tube
Reagent

Crystals/Particles
Metal mesh

C Clear plastic bag

Figure 11 – The tube and bag roadside screening device.

marked around the circumference of the tube about halfway along the length of the silica gel indicates the 80 mg limit. If the breath alcohol leads to a colour change beyond this mark, then the test is considered positive and the motorist is likely to be taken to the police station for further testing. The third part of the apparatus is the plastic bag (C), which has a narrow rubber or plastic neck to form a close fitting seal with the lower end of the glass tube. It is usual for the bag, which is of 1 litre capacity, to be used for about 10 tests before being replaced. Between tests the bag must be completely flattened out to ensure that the same volume of breath is used for inflation in every case.

Before the various parts can be fitted together for use, the sealed end of the chemical tube must be removed, usually with a small serrated knife fitted into the side of the box for the set of ten tubes. The sharp edges formed on the tube are no danger as one end is then covered with the plastic mouthpiece and the other by the tube connector on the bag. The success and reliability of the test are dependent upon enough air being blown in a single continuous breath to inflate the bag completely in a period of time between 10 and 20 seconds long. Refusal to comply with these requirements has been accepted in court as refusal to supply a breath sample. Whilst alcoholic breath is being blown through the tube a noticeable rise in temperature occurs as the chemical reaction takes place and the green colour develops along the tube.

The instructions for carrying out the test particularly caution against using the equipment on drinkers if fewer than 20 minutes have elapsed since the last alcoholic drink was taken. This is because artificially high readings are obtained due to residual mouth alcohol which takes up to 15 minutes to disappear. At the same time, misleadingly low readings will also be obtained if alcohol is still being absorbed from the stomach into the blood stream. For these reasons, the delay between drinking and being tested is essential.

Similarly, anybody who has been sick is likely to produce anomalously high readings because of stomach alcohol brought into the mouth. It has also been found that smoking immediately prior to the test can lead to different colour reactions due to the constituents of the cigarette smoke masking the true colour change of the chemical reagents.

Methods of confusing the test by sucking peppermints or drinking water or coffee are of no value as they have been shown to have no effect upon the alcohol already absorbed into the blood stream. It has been established that consumption of large quantities of fruit or fruit juices can lead to a slightly higher than normal blood alcohol figure. However, nobody existing on a diet of fruit and juices is likely to give a positive breath test as it takes at least 500 g of fruit to raise the blood alcohol level by as little as 8 mg and it would be necessary to consume about 9 lbs of fruit in one hour to risk reaching the limit[11]. The breath test is not concerned with the origin of the alcohol it detects and, as far as the inability to drive matters, alcohol from one source is as dangerous as alcohol from another.

The tube and bag device can be manufactured in such a way that it will produce a measurable response to levels of alcohol as low as 30 mg. The design is modified either with a slightly longer or shorter reagent packing or by altering the position of the pass/fail measuring line. A colour change can be detected on the reagent with alcohol levels as low as 5 mg but reliable quantitative measurement at this level is not possible.

The Alcotest has been imitated and modified many times and a number of tube and bag devices exist based upon the dichromate/sulphuric acid reaction. The Czechoslovakian version of the tube was known as the 'Detalkohol' and in Hungary and Romania devices were named 'Pluralkol' and 'Alcosoop' respectively.

Limits of accuracy

In tube and bag testing devices, the length of the green zone produced should increase in proportion to the amount of alcohol in the sample. To achieve a high degree of success at the legal limit, it has to be made sensitive enough also to fail some people who are below the limit[12]. Within the first month of its application in Great Britain in 1967, of the 927 drivers who gave a positive reaction at the kerbside, 168 (18%) were below the 80 mg level on analysis of the blood or urine samples. While some of these may have fallen below the limit because of the delay before blood sampling, it appeared that the possible error on the breath tube could be quite high. This contention was supported by research work carried out by Dr G G Muir and his colleagues which was published in the learned scientific journal *Nature*[13]. Their work showed that 77%

of their subjects giving positive breath tests using the Alcotest 80 apparatus actually had blood alcohol levels below the 80 mg limit. Even more serious was the observation that 62% of subjects possessing less than 50 mg failed the breath test.

Further criticism of the Alcotest 80 was made by the Blennerhassett Committee[14] in 1976 when it was pointed out that only 70% of those apprehended by failing the roadside test were eventually found to be above the 80 mg limit. This was because 10% were eliminated by a second screening breath test at the police station and 20% were found to be below the 80 mg on analysis of the blood or urine sample. The committee also emphasised that many of the discrepancies were likely to be due to misreading the colour change under poor illumination, although delays in getting motorists to the police station for further tests also played some part in these results.

Although the roadside screening test does not need to be totally accurate in the sense that the results are not used as the basis for prosecution, it is essential that any degree of error should be kept to a minimum. Any such test producing erroneously high reading leads to large numbers of drivers being asked to go to the police station to provide evidential samples which are then shown to be below the legal limit. This can represent an enormous waste of time, money and effort which could better be expended. It was this reasoning which led the Blennerhassett Committee to recommend that screening tests would be easier to carry out with devices which gave a clear fail/pass indication.

Electronic screening devices

Fortunately, during the 1970s a great deal of research work was carried out in the designing of portable electronic devices which could be used to measure environmental and atmospheric vapours and this led to the development of two main types of instruments which were suitable for the detection of breath alcohol and which met all the necessary criteria in terms of portability and reliability. These instruments either used fuel cells or semiconductors as the sensors for the alcohol.

Fuel cell instruments

Fuel cells are devices in which an electric current is produced as a result of a chemical reaction taking place on the surface of an electrode system[15]. For the measurement of alcohol, the reaction employed is the oxidation of the alcohol/ethanol to acetaldehyde (ethanal) and this is carried out in a fuel cell consisting of a deposit of gold and platinum on a porous disc[16]. This is the main operational feature in the 'Alcolmeter' series of instruments which includes a wide range of screening devices and evidential breath alcohol analysers used extensively throughout the world.

Fuel cells are highly sensitive detectors and only a small sample of breath is actually required, most of that blown by the subject being allowed to go straight through the sample tube with a small quantity being diverted to the cell. The basic operation of the Alcolmeter unit is illustrated in Figure 12 overleaf. It uses a two-button control system and is first set with button B depressed so that the piston is lowered. When button A is pressed the piston is raised, removing the atmosphere from around the working electrode and replacing it by a breath sample drawn in from that being blown through the sample tube. In the Alcolmeters, the small electric current produced as a result of the alcohol reaction on the electrode can be used to give either a digital display, move a needle on a meter or trigger a series of lights appropriate to the breath or blood alcohol level. The test takes only a few seconds to carry out as it involves blowing about 1.2 litres of air through a small sample tube with virtually no resistance to the blowing. The read button has to be held down for about 30 seconds for the true result of the test to be obtained on the display panel, but with the series of pass/fail lights many drunk drivers produce a positive result in only a few seconds[17]. The standardisation of these instruments is equally easy to carry out using appropriate alcohol in argon gas mixtures.

Alcolmeters are now used very widely throughout the world including Australia, Spain and the USA (where they are known under the trade name 'Alcosensor'). The version used by the police in Great Britain is the Alcolmeter S–L2A (as

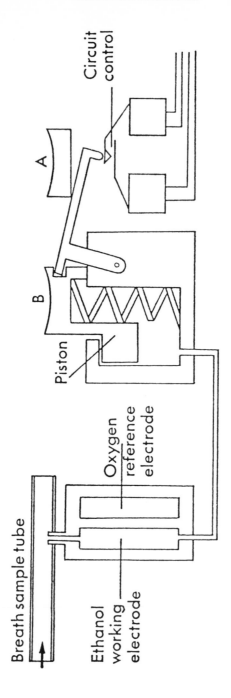

Figure 12 – Operating mechanism for the Alcolmeter S–L2A fuel cell screening breath testing instrument.

illustrated in Figure 13). This has two sets of lights: the first pair of small lights will tell the operator if the subject has blown long enough and hard enough to provide an acceptable sample and the second set of lights (the 'traffic lights') will indicate if the person blowing is above or below the legal limit. Subjects who are just below the limit will produce both the orange and red lights together and those over the legal limit will light up just the red one. An experienced operator can obtain a fairly clear idea of the intoxication of the person blowing from the rapidity with which the red light is produced. Assessments that have been made since these instruments were introduced by the police in 1980 have shown that they have fully come up to expectations in terms of reliability and

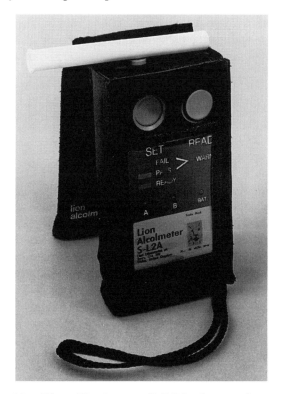

Figure 13 – Lion Alcolmeter S–L2A electronic roadside screening instrument.

accuracy and have led to a reduction in the number of false positives from screening tests[18]. This has been further substantiated by in-depth comparisons between various blood samples and breath samples measured on the S–D2 digital display version of the Alcolmeter[19].

As a result, the Alcolmeter S–L2A is now the most common device used for roadside screening tests in Great Britain, although it has not totally displaced the tube and bag devices. More advanced fuel cell instruments are now available, including the Lion Alcolmeter SL–400 (Figure 14) and the Dräger Alcotest 7410 (Figure 15). These are being used increasingly in industrial situations as well as for drink-driving tests.

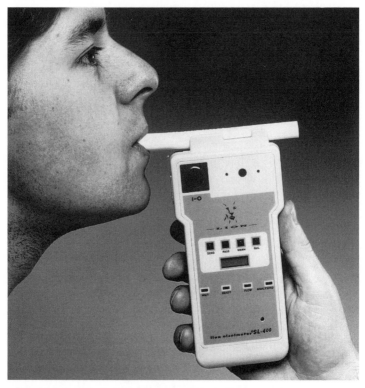

Figure 14 – Lion Alcolmeter SL–400 electronic roadside screening instrument.

Figure 15 – Dräger Alcotest 7410 electronic roadside screening instrument.

Semiconductor instruments

A variety of instruments now exist based upon the change in resistance of semiconductors when substances are deposited on their surfaces. Under normal conditions, the semiconductor detector will respond to a wide range of organic compounds but, if the sample passing over the surface is breath, there are unlikely to be any significant concentrations of organic vapours other than alcohol present. A response will, in some instances, occur due to fumes from cough mixture or vinegar if these have been taken.

The detector operates on the principle that the change in resistance of the semiconductor can be related to the amount of alcohol in the breath sample and the electric current flowing through the electronic circuit proportional to this change can be used either to trigger a series of lights or to illuminate a digital display. As the electronic systems are relatively simple, fairly cheap instruments can be constructed. One such device is used by the Japanese police and is designed in the form of a police baton with the sensor at one end. If a driver is stopped, the policeman only has to put the baton close to the person's face for it to light up in response to any alcohol in the exhaled breath. Passive detector systems of this type are being used increasingly around the world as they overcome the obvious problems that arise for police officers trying to smell intoxicants on motorists' breath.

Self-testing devices

Because of the increasing number of roadside tests carried out by the police and tighter law enforcement, there is a continuous demand by responsible motorists for devices they can use personally to monitor their own breath before driving. This was particularly seen in France during 1978 when a law was introduced enabling police to carry out random spot tests on motorists at any time and was strongly enforced with an extremely high number of tests being conducted. An immediate market for self-testing devices arose which could not be satisfied by the very few suppliers marketing reliable products.

Over the years, various manufacturers have tried to market tube and bag devices, often at Christmas time. Unfortunately, many of these have been inferior, inaccurate and unreliable with insufficient instructions for their correct use. Any drinker relying on these is often in real danger of risking his or her driving licence. By using such inferior systems, it is possible for people to be misled into believing they are fit to drive when they are not. This has resulted in court cases in which magistrates have convicted motorists of driving with blood alcohol levels above the limit although they have only driven after self-applied breath tests indicated that they were below the limit.

Other self-testing devices include simplified versions of semiconductor electronic instruments which are now on sale to the general public in many countries. Some of these operate using a series of lights so that if the breath only contains a small amount of alcohol a green light comes up, if the blood alcohol level is more than half the legal limit an orange light comes up and if it is over the limit a red light glows. Correct operation of these instruments requires the user to blow steadily for 4–6 seconds as there is usually no instrumental control to define the amount of breath measured or passed over the surface of the semiconductor. Other versions of the same system employ a coloured display scale marked with ranges of breath or blood alcohol values.

There is undoubtedly a need to ensure that anything for self-testing sold or available for use by the motorist does at least satisfy certain minimum criteria laid down by the Government or by a recognised standards authority. Certainly, the coin-in-the-slot machines which are making their appearance in some public houses should only be permitted for use if they comply with defined levels of accuracy and reliability and are regularly serviced. Even then it must be made quite clear that the result of a screening test is only an indication of a particular alcohol level and that the reliability of the result depends upon the quality of the testing device used and upon the user of the machine complying with the required procedures.

The big problem with all self-testing devices is that the user may produce an artificially high value due to giving a sample when there is still residual mouth alcohol present from the last drink. Alternatively, and more dangerously, there may be a low result if alcohol is still being absorbed into the blood stream. As a result, the drinking motorist may start to drive whilst below the legal limit but with a steadily increasing blood alcohol level. Therefore, self-testers should always check themselves at least twice with a thirty minute interval between the tests to determine if the blood and/or breath alcohol level is rising or falling.

Chapter 6

EVIDENTIAL BREATH TESTING

" 'Yes, I have a pair of eyes', replied Sam,
'and that's just it. If they was a pair o' patent
double million magnifyin' gas microscopes of
hextra power, p'raps I might be able to see
through a flight o' stairs and a deal door; but
bein' only eyes, you see my wision's limited.' "

Charles Dickens

Since the first roadside breath testing machines were introduced in the USA in the 1930s, enormous advances have been made and a wide variety of devices have been invented for sampling breath in different situations. At this stage we are now in the third generation of evidential breath testing machines, having advanced a long way from the early days of equipment which relied heavily on the use of colour changes occurring in aqueous solutions of chemical reagents and that had a number of disadvantages in terms of transportation and operation. Many of the problems associated with earlier evidential machines were overcome with the development of computer controlled systems and the use of electronic circuits incorporating fuel cells, infra-red detectors or gas chromatographs.

Recent and on-going developments are such that modern instruments are designed to be fully operator-proof by being completely automatic, self-zeroing, self-checking instruments producing results which in most circumstances can fully take the place of blood or urine samples. These advances have all been achieved in a space of about 40 years and progressively more and more countries are accepting the obvious advantages presented by being able to obtain immediate results based upon breath samples as compared with the considerable delays involved in the sampling and analysis of blood and urine.

93

Quantitative measurement of alcohol can be carried out in a variety of ways using either chemical or physical methods. The first generation evidential breath testing devices were based upon wet chemical solutions and the only one which met with any long term success was the original 'Breathalyzer'.

The Breathalyzer

It is unfortunate that this name, although spelt differently, has also become the colloquial term for the tube and bag device currently employed for screening tests in so many countries. The apparatus to which it correctly refers was originally described[1,2] in 1954 and various modified forms of the instrument have been used extensively in the USA, Canada and Australia for screening purposes and for evidential tests for presentation in court. The Breathalyzer was manufactured in Europe under the name 'Ethanographe' and was used for a number of years after 1968 by the police in Northern Ireland.

The general operation of the instrument can be followed from the simplified diagram in Figure 16. Breath is blown into the apparatus causing the piston (A) to rise to the top of the cylinder (B). By turning the control valve (C), the measured volume is then forced, by the falling piston, through the heated solution of potassium dichromate and sulphuric acid (D). Any alcohol present in the breath causes the formation of green chromium sulphate. The intensity of the colour change is related to the amount of alcohol in the breath and is compared to a blank unreacted solution (E), the absolute value being measured on the photo-electric circuit. The meter (F) is calibrated to give a direct reading of the concentration of alcohol in the blood on the basis of the relationship to the breath alcohol content. The case housing the apparatus incorporates a heating unit which warms the breath sample to 50°C (122°F) and the test ampoules to 65°C (149°F) before the analysis is carried out.

The various forms of the Breathalyzer have been well tried around the world and have given highly accurate and reproducible results comparable with those obtained from analysis of blood samples[3,4]. Developments in the model known as the 'Breathalyzer 1000' led to the machine being one of those evaluated by the British Government during the first series of field trials on evidential breath testing instruments[5], but it was not ultimately recommended for use by the police.

Its main disadvantage was that it used acidic solutions, with all the attendant problems of corrosion and disposal. It has now been superseded by the development of other evidential instruments.

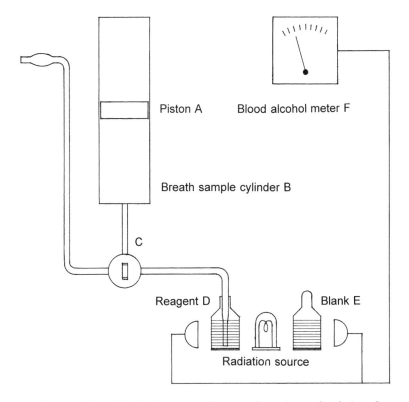

Piston A

Blood alcohol meter F

Breath sample cylinder B

C

Reagent D   Blank E

Radiation source

Figure 16 – Block diagram illustrating the principle of operation of the early evidential breath testing instrument 'The Breathalyzer'.

Gas chromatographic instruments

One of the most sensitive methods of analysis, known as gas chromatography, is described in Chapter 7. This rather cumbersome laboratory procedure was ingeniously modified into a more portable form for use as an on-the-spot testing device[6]. In this particular design, the driver's breath was collected by blowing into a specially calibrated syringe from which a measured volume was pumped into the separating column for study by the gas chromatographic method. The various gaseous constituents of the breath, including any alcohol, were detected using what is known as a flame ionisation detector. In this, the small amount of sample, taken after the subject's lungs have been emptied, is separated into individual chemical components by passage through the chromatographic column and the various substances are then made to produce an electronic signal by burning them in a small gas jet in the detector. A separate electronic signal is obtained for each substance burnt in the flame. The main disadvantage of this method is that it needs a supply of a gas mixture of nitrogen and hydrogen from a cylinder for its operation.

The 'Mark IV Gas Chromatograph Intoximeter' form of this instrument[7] only uses a minute sample of breath obtained from deep inside the lungs. Because it actually separates the breath components, it is specific in its measurement of alcohol and, after calibration with standards, will produce a quick, accurate measurement of the blood alcohol level presented both as a digital display and on a strip chart or printout. The instrument has met with wide acceptance in North America, Europe and Australia and has been used for evidential purposes in a number of countries. The helium gas supply for the instrument is contained in a small cylinder inside the instrument case and it can operate on either a mains power supply or a 12-volt car battery. This instrument was also evaluated in the first of the British evidential field trials[5] but was not re-assessed during the second field trial or recommended for use by the police.

Infra-red analysers

The evidential machines most widely used throughout the world at present are those based upon the absorption of infra-red energy by the alcohol molecules contained in the samples of breath blown through a fixed volume sample cell. A very extensive range of these instruments now exists and several different models are in use in various countries and states.

All the instruments are dependent upon the fact that if infra-red radiation in the wavelength range of 3.39–3.48 µm is passed through a specified volume of alcohol, then the extent of the absorption of the energy (measured as a diminution of the original energy) is a quantitative measure of the amount of alcohol in the sample. The success of such instruments relies upon the absence from the breath of any other substance which might also absorb at the selective wavelength[8]. Because of this, detectors have to be incorporated to detect and correct for the presence of such things as acetone, a contaminant particularly present in the breath of diabetics, and for any environmentally absorbed solvents[9]. It must, however, be emphasised that in the vast majority of cases the possibility of any interfering substance being present and leading to a false positive result is very small.

The acetone effect

Because acetone, occurring naturally at low levels in breath, is capable of absorbing infra-red radiation at 3.39 µm, it can be mistaken for alcohol by these machines. In the second generation evidential breath testing machines, the problem of the acetone factor was overcome in two ways. These methods involved either detecting the acetone at another wavelength or with a different detector and applying a correction to the apparent alcohol value, or by measuring the alcohol at a wavelength at which the acetone does not respond. Both approaches are employed in instruments adopted for law enforcement purposes.

Before evidential breath testing was introduced into Great Britain, the government studied the suitability of using infra-red analysers for this purpose. In the first field trials, the 'CMI Intoxylizer 4011A' was assessed. This instrument measured alcohol at 3.48 μm and had a built-in deduction for the small infra-red absorption[5] due to water and to low levels of acetone at this particular wavelength. The sample cell in the Intoxylizer had a capacity of 600 mL and the infra-red beam was reflected back and forth several times in order to obtain a high level of absorption which was relatively easy to measure. Ultimately, this particular machine was not recommended for adoption by the police in Great Britain.

Two other infra-red absorption machines were evaluated in the second series of field trials[10] and these were then adopted and used by the police throughout Great Britain. The two machines were the 'Camic Infrared Breath Analyser' and the 'Lion Intoximeter 3000'.

Camic breath analysers
The Camic machine measures the alcohol at 3.47 μm and it is claimed that water vapour, carbon monoxide, carbon dioxide and acetone do not interfere with these measurements when at normal concentrations. In the field trials, it was shown that excellent agreement was obtained between pairs of breath samples and the machines gave very few maintenance problems. Since May 1983, Camic machines have been used by police forces in the north-east of England and in Scotland and many thousands of successful tests have been carried out on them.

Lion Intoximeter 3000
The Lion Intoximeter 3000 is a British version (made in Wales) of a very well proven American machine (Figure 17). It is, at present, the most extensively used evidential breath testing machine in the United Kingdom and has been in use since 1983. It is a computer-operated instrument that functions completely automatically once its action has been initiated by typing in the operator's name and personal code. After that, it blows air through a special alcohol solution to give an alcohol vapour standard corresponding to the legal breath alcohol limit. It purges itself between samples and has fixed periods of three minutes for valid breath samples to be

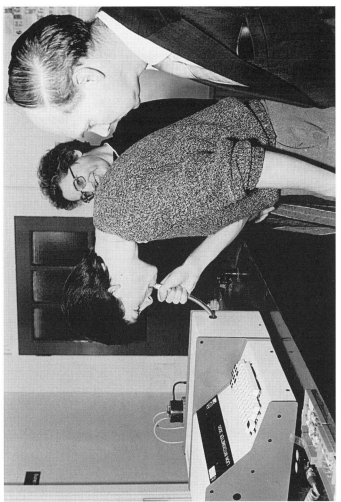

Figure 17 – The author testing people on the Lion Intoximeter 3000 evidential breath testing machine at the University of Greenwich.

provided. In order to supply a valid breath sample, a subject has to blow a minimum of 1.5 litres of air, which is monitored by a thermistor. At the end of the exhalation of the breath sample, a small volume, about 70 mL, is passed into the alcohol detector cell of the machine (Figure 18) and the infra-red absorption of this sample is measured against that of a sample of alcohol-free air in the adjacent comparator cell. The signals from these volumes are measured quantitatively with respect to zero baseline conditions and to the known alcohol standards.

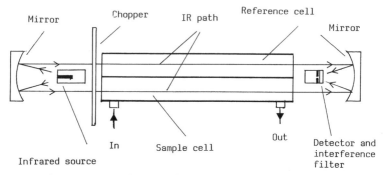

Figure 18 – Diagram illustrating the principle of operation of the Lion Intoximeter 3000 evidential breath testing instrument.

Because it measures alcohol at 3.39 μm, at which acetone also has a positive absorption, a secondary semiconductor detector is incorporated which gives a major response to any acetone in the breath sample. The signal from the semiconductor is then used to apply an appropriate correction to the apparent alcohol value in order to produce a true alcohol in breath result. This machine also records the acetone level in terms of 'Trace Acetone', 'Moderate Acetone' or 'Large Acetone' on the breath alcohol result slip printed out after the subject has been tested and the test cycle has been completed. In the UK field trials, the Lion Intoximeter 3000 was also shown to give good agreement between a person's consecutive breath samples, with 94.3% of all duplicate breath samples giving results which agreed within 5 μg of each other and only 1.3% producing two results differing by more than 10 μg.

Despite the extensive studies to which both the Camic and the Lion machines were subjected and the fact that they had to meet criteria much stricter than those applied in any other country, their introduction for evidential breath alcohol measurement in May 1983 quickly led to a great deal of criticism on television and radio[11], which was followed about nine months later by a powerful and prolonged press campaign conducted by the *Daily Express*[12]. The reasons for this are discussed more fully in Chapter 8 as they arose from the very badly written law introduced[13] by the British Government. However, there is no doubt that the use of these two types of machine in place of blood and urine sampling achieved an enormous saving in police time and money and meant that motorists did not have to wait for several weeks before knowing if they were over the legal limit and likely to be prosecuted for drink-driving. The number of cases in which any controversy has arisen about the validity of the breath alcohol results is very small in relation to the many thousands of tests carried out, although it is very important that nobody should be convicted for being above the legal limit due to any form of defective measurement. Comparisons which have been carried out on breath alcohol levels and corresponding blood alcohol values have shown[14] that there is a very close relationship between the two and, if anything, the breath alcohol values are lower than the blood alcohol values and work more to the motorists' advantage.

Evidential fuel cell instruments

A third group of evidential breath testing machines is based upon the fuel cell, as used in the roadside screening Alcolmeters and Alcosensors. These incorporate the same breath sensing unit as that used in the screening devices as described in Chapter 5. However, in the evidential models of the instruments, the sensor is maintained at a slightly elevated temperature in order to reduce the reaction time. Any signal then obtained is used to produce a digital display of the corresponding breath alcohol level and to activate a printer to produce a printed record of the results. Early versions of the evidential Alcolmeter gave satisfactory service in Northern

Ireland for many years and they are also used in Australia and Spain. They are the most portable of all the evidential machines and particularly suitable for large scale 'booze bus' roadside testing.

The fuel cell instruments have the great advantage that they do not respond to hydrocarbons, acetone or most other substances and they are almost totally selective for alcohol in the breath.

Problems with evidential breath testing

The commonest claims made against breath testing machines now fall into two main groups. There are those which are based upon the idea that the recorded values have been artificially increased as a result of the motorist having previously inhaled or absorbed alcohol or other solvents to which they have been subjected for prolonged periods. The other group of defences are claims that the results must be wrong because the motorist used a mouth spray, a deodoriser, an asthma inhaler or a throat treatment shortly before being tested.

Many tests have been carried out to measure the effects of absorbed solvents from polluted atmospheres. The one consistent result from such tests is that it is possible to produce abnormal breath alcohol values immediately after a person has been exposed to a solvent atmosphere for a prolonged period of several hours. However, the tests also show that this result disappears very rapidly and usually diminishes to virtually zero after about 20–30 minutes[15]. All the studies have shown that there is no long-term retention of the artificially elevated values sufficient to produce misleading results on breath analysis equipment because of the delays that occur in initially stopping the motorist and carrying out the evidential breath testing[16]. Obviously, this does not deal with the problem of the motorist who spends several hours, say, in a solvent laden atmosphere spraying a car without adequate ventilation or protective clothing and who is stopped for an evidential test at the roadside, as in Northern Ireland or Victoria, Australia, almost immediately after leaving work. In some instances, the residual solvent effect can still be responsible for putting a motorist above the legal limit but these circumstances will almost certainly produce two widely differing apparent breath alcohol values.

It must be emphasised that any abnormal results are due far more to solvents retained within the mouth, throat and windpipe rather than to solvents which have actually entered the blood stream. Any accumulation of an elevated blood solvent level requires a build-up of what would be a high solvent level in the blood from a correspondingly low solvent vapour level in the air inhaled by the person working in the polluted atmosphere without adequate (and legally required) protection. Chemical theory itself suggests that this effective reversal of solvent concentrations is highly unlikely and practical studies have shown that any solvent levels built up in the body by this means are so low that recovery is very rapid. Because of this, defences based upon the possible inhalation of solvents are usually unsuccessful.

However, the effects of the use of various mouth sprays have to be treated with care and caution. It is quite true to say that many mouth sprays and related medicinal treatments do contain alcohol or other substances that can produce positive results on the breath testing machines. The results from these sprays are similar to what has already been referred to as 'the mouth alcohol effect'.

The effect is the same as the production of falsely elevated breath alcohol values as a result of breath testing a person very soon after he or she has last had an alcoholic drink. The results then include not only the alcohol present in the breath arising from the blood alcohol level, but also residual alcohol vapour from alcohol within the saliva and surface fluids in the mouth. Because of this, the police are advised to wait for several minutes before carrying out any breath testing if a motorist claims to have drunk alcohol within the previous 20 minutes.

The use of mouth sprays can simulate the mouth alcohol effect, so a person who has used a spray or mouth freshener also should not be breath tested for 15–20 minutes after use of the spray. Studies on this effect have shown that, irrespective of how it may have arisen, it will generally disappear completely within a 12–15 minute time period[17].

The interesting thing about the mouth alcohol effect is that whether it has arisen from actual drinking of alcohol or from use of sprays, it follows a very strict mathematical law. This is a half-life rule which shows that, whatever the breath alcohol level from the effect may be at any stage, the value will be halved every 60–70 seconds. So a result of 80 µg becomes 40 µg a minute later, 20 µg a minute after that, then 10 µg after that and 5 µg a minute following. This means that an artificial 80 µg value follows a sharply falling curve and disappears to about 1 µg after roughly seven minutes. There is no long-term retention of the mouth alcohol effect.

The reason the mouth alcohol effect disappears rapidly is due to of the normal loss of vapour from breathing and opening and shutting the mouth and because of the natural washing of the inside of the mouth from salivating and swallowing. These factors even lead to the loss of trapped alcohol from around dentures.

Third generation instruments

There is no doubt that the overwhelming success in evidential breath testing rests with the infra-red analysers. The new generation instruments now available have been designed to deal with the problems of acetone and inhaled solvent detection, big differences between consecutive sample values, and the volume of air required for a valid sample. In these respects, a great deal has been learnt from very controversial court cases which have occurred since the introduction of evidential breath testing machines.

Specifications for these instruments have been developed very much along British guidelines which have also served as a basis for consideration by the European Commission. There is now a great deal of international co-operation over this subject in the hope that a set of criteria can be produced for evidential breath testing machines that will meet with wide agreement[18].

Figure 19 – The Lion Intoxilyzer 6000 infra-red evidential breath testing equipment.

The new instruments, such as the Lion Intoxilyzer 6000 (Figure 19), are designed to measure sample absorptions at several infra-red wavelengths and to balance the signal strengths against each other. They introduce a whole new realm of sophistication into evidential breath measurement. However, even these instruments are unlikely to lead to the total removal of additional legal safeguards in most countries with optional blood sample and/or back-up confirmatory tests.

In matters relating to drinking and driving, it is always essential to obtain public co-operation and acceptance if possible dissatisfaction with the law is to be avoided and police/public relations are not to be undermined. The wide variety of breath testing equipment now available makes it essential that all instruments are very carefully evaluated before being recommended for use by the police[19] and that this is backed up by regular maintenance and servicing.

All quantitative methods of detection suffer from limitations and have varying degrees of accuracy. Because of this, statistical surveys are required to establish the level of reproducibility that can be expected in any particular type of instrument. An allowance must always be made for any constant instrumental error that might exist within the recorded value. Public confidence in evidential breath testing has be developed steadily and in places such as Northern Ireland, in which drivers were given a choice between providing an evidential breath test or giving a blood sample for analysis, 90% were happy to accept the value from the breath test[20].

Needless to say, the field of breath testing is not one in which science is standing still. Further improvements are already in hand, with investigations including the use of laser techniques and the development of instruments for detecting other drugs as well as alcohol. There is no bright future for the drinking or drugged driver!

Chapter 7

BLOOD AND URINE TESTS

"He did not wear his scarlet coat,
For blood and wine are red,
And blood and wine were on his hands
When they found him with the dead."

Oscar Wilde

Because it is the alcohol in the blood which is responsible for the impairment of a person's ability to drive, it is obvious that blood is the ideal sample to take for analysis. The study of any other body fluid automatically involves the use of conversion factors, either directly or indirectly. However, in many ways breath is a much better substance to sample in the sense that it is non-invasive and can be tested without having to call out a medical practitioner. Nevertheless, in most countries breath is still only used for screening purposes, while it is blood or urine samples (and sometimes saliva) taken at the police station which are employed for the evidential values.

Body fluids

As has been previously discussed, it is because of the dynamic equilibrium that exists in the distribution of alcohol between body fluids and tissue (see Chapter 2) that it is possible to sample any portion of the body and be able to assess the blood alcohol level from it. This, of course, only applies if about one hour has elapsed after drinking has ceased. However, it should be borne in mind that, for a roadside screening test, a breath sample is the obvious choice as the expired air is in constant equilibrium with the blood in the lungs so that the breath alcohol concentration should give a reliable indication of the blood alcohol level. As evidential breath testing becomes more widely accepted by motorists, there is a progressive reduction in the number seeking to exercise any option that might exist to provide a blood or urine sample as an alternative. However, the need for reliable blood alcohol analysis methods remains, not only for forensic purposes but also for clinical and food analysis reasons.

As blood samples are usually provided under medical supervision only after fairly lengthy delays at the police station, the equilibrium conditions between the body fluids are almost certainly reached. It is well known that the delays which occur prior to the provision of the samples act to the advantage of the driver as the alcohol in his body is being steadily metabolised and eliminated all the time. It has been shown that in Great Britain the combination of delays that can occur prior to the provision of blood samples means that in reality the effective blood alcohol limit is about 30 mg above the legal limit[1].

Urine samples

In many instances, drivers have deep-rooted objections to providing blood samples and opt to provide samples of their urine instead. They are, of course, unaware that scientific evaluations indicate that urine is less capable of providing reliable figures than is blood.

The errors that can occur with urine samples arise partially from the delay in the alcohol being eliminated from the body fluids into the bladder and partially from variations in observed values for converting urine alcohol figures to blood alcohol figures. Under the British law two samples of urine are requested from the driver. The first is discarded as it is possible that it represents elimination by the kidneys prior to the breath test being taken and is not necessarily representative of the blood alcohol level. The second sample, which should be requested no less than half an hour after the first, is a freshly eliminated specimen and more comparable with the blood alcohol level. However, it must be remembered that urine is a 'dead' liquid and once passed from the kidneys it is not in dynamic equilibrium with the other body fluids. Over a period of time the alcohol in the bladder may be increased or reduced depending upon the concentration of the alcohol in the urine still being filtered by the kidneys.

The legal limit for alcohol in urine specified by the Road Safety Act 1967 and maintained by subsequent Road Traffic Acts, is 107 mg. This is considered to be the equivalent to a blood alcohol level of 80 mg on the basis of a 1.3 conversion factor. The origin and justification of this particular value has come under strong criticism on several occasions. As long ago as 1941 it was shown[2] that the conversion factor could vary between 1.2 and 1.4 depending upon the specific gravity of the urine*.

A statistical survey of 10,000 blood and urine tests, carried out in 1962 by Dr W Froentjes[3], showed that there was a very poor correlation on the 1.33 urine/blood conversion factor and that a more correct figure would be of the order of 1.54. During 1966, the report of a similar comparative study was published in the *British Medical Journal*[4] which showed that there is virtually no simple correlation between the figures for alcohol in urine and those for alcohol in blood sampled at the same time. The factors varied from about 1.00 to 2.50 and averaged out to 1.44; still higher than the accepted 1.33.

Urine samples are, therefore, unsatisfactory in many different ways and should only be legally accepted in those instances in which there is a clear medical or deeply religious reason for not providing a blood sample. Thus, someone suffering from haemophilia, or a Jehovah's Witness, might justifiably object to providing blood samples. The problem does not, of course, occur if the law provides initially for evidential breath samples.

Blood samples

Although blood samples may be taken in a variety of ways and from many different sites, it is most common for a hypodermic syringe to be used to obtain a volume of venous blood from one arm. Although adequate analytical results can be obtained from very small volumes of blood, the use of capillary blood samples, obtained by squeezing out a few drops from a pinprick in an ear lobe or thumb, is now relatively uncommon.

---

* Specific gravity is defined as the weight of a known volume of a substance compared to the weight of the same volume of water.

This is particularly because the use of capillary blood samples came in for some fairly considerable criticism and doubt was cast upon the reliability of pin-prick samples due to four main sources of error[5,6]:

1. Capillary blood is likely to give a high alcohol value as it contains proportionally more plasma than does venous blood.

2. While the drops are being squeezed from the finger, evaporation of the alcohol may lead to a lower figure.

3. As the sample containers are only partially filled, evaporation continues from the surface of the sample into the void volume above until such a time that the sample is refrigerated. This again contributes to a lower recorded alcohol figure.

4. Some samples clot inside the containers despite the presence of anti-coagulants and any test therefore tends to be carried out on the plasma enriched fluid portion giving rise to a higher alcohol figure.

So capillary blood samples cannot be considered to be reliable for evidential analysis and it is necessary to resort to the hypodermic syringe for more suitable samples.

Sample kits

The taking of blood samples at a police station has to be carried out by a Forensic Medical Examiner who will use a standard pre-packed sampling kit. The main items of the kits (Figure 20) are a hypodermic syringe and needle in a sterile pack, two small sample bottles with self-sealing rubber caps and two fixed seal security containers for the sample bottles. The syringe is used to take up to a 5 mL sample which is divided between the two sample bottles by piercing their rubber caps. Each sample bottle is then sealed in one of the plastic security containers with a tear-off seal top which will show clear signs of any attempts at tampering. Coagulation or bacterial decomposition of samples is prevented by a small amount of preservative previously sealed inside the sample

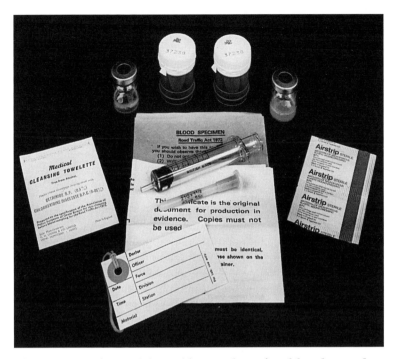

Figure 20 – Kit used for taking and storing blood samples.

bottles. Security and integrity of the samples is further maintained by the same sample number being printed on the two sample bottles and the two security containers. One of the two portions of the blood sample is for the motorist to take in order to obtain a private analysis, if required. In order to prevent attempts at tampering with the sample, it is packed inside a special self-sealing envelope which is signed across the seams.

Other items in the kit include a non-alcoholic disinfection swab, a plaster for covering the puncture spot and identity labels for fixing to the sample bottles. For urine samples larger containers are used (Figure 21) but similar precautions are taken in the labelling and packaging.

Enormous advances have been made in recent years to improve blood and urine sampling procedures. These followed

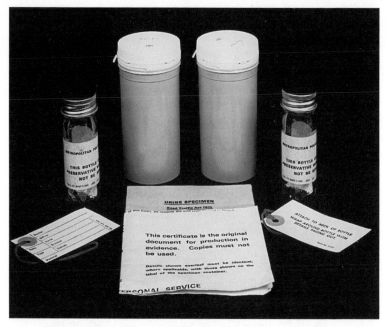

Figure 21 – Kit used for storing urine samples.

substantial criticisms[7] of the sometimes lax and unreliable methods and equipment employed in the years immediately following the introduction of the Road Safety Act 1967.

Both blood and urine samples should always be refrigerated as soon as possible and kept in this state until required for analysis. The methods available for analysing such samples fall into three main groups:

1. Chemical methods.

2. Biochemical methods.

3. Physico-chemical methods.

Chemical methods of analysis

When the laws in Sweden, Norway and the USA first permitted the taking of blood and urine samples for alcohol analysis, the procedures available were less sophisticated than those now used and were mainly limited to methods based upon chemical and biochemical oxidation reactions. The groundwork for chemical methods of analysis was laid as long ago[8] as 1905, since when substantial improvements in techniques and accuracy[9] have taken place. However, the speed and reproducibility attainable with gas chromatography (page 114) mean that in most industrialised countries chemical methods of blood and urine analysis are now rarely used.

The chemical methods[10,11] recommended were all based upon the oxidation of the alcohol by the use of excess hot acidified potassium dichromate (see Appendix), the amount of alcohol in the original sample being ascertained by determining the amount of potassium dichromate used for the oxidation after measuring the quantity remaining at the end of the reaction. Results by these chemical oxidation procedures are accurate to within ±5%, so a value of 80 mg could mean a possible true value between 76 mg and 84 mg.

Biochemical methods of analysis

All biochemical methods of analysis are based upon the oxidation of the alcohol by the action of enzymes. Only one procedure has become clearly established as being highly reliable, reproducible and easily carried out. This is based upon the conversion of alcohol to acetaldehyde by the action of an enzyme (an organic catalyst) known as alcohol dehydrogenase (ADH). The method is of value because it is virtually specific for alcohol when applied to blood and urine samples[12].

The amount of alcohol in the sample is assessed by measuring the intensity of a coloured compound produced in proportion to the quantity of alcohol present. Unfortunately, a single analysis can take up to an hour to perform, although it lends itself readily to automation for dealing with large numbers of samples and the average analysis time can be reduced to less than 10 minutes. A number of commercial kits are available for one-off determinations of blood samples and these are used in clinical studies. A study of these kits[13] showed that, while they were all based on the same basic enzymatic process, they did vary in their sensitivities and reproducibilities. In general, such kits are capable of achieving an accuracy to within ±6–8%. The ADH enzymatic oxidation method is used in Sweden as a secondary check on results obtained for the analysis of blood samples by the chromatographic method.

Because they can be used for one-off analyses, the ADH kits are used extensively in hospitals for rapid studies on road casualties who may also appear to have symptoms arising from head injuries. The ADH system is very versatile and various modifications have made it applicable to a range of fluids[14]. It has also been used in a non-invasive roadside screening system based upon the alcohol content of saliva[15].

Gas chromatography

The most versatile method of chemical separation and analysis which has been devised for volatile substances is certainly gas chromatography (GC). During the past 30 years, the equipment has become a standard item in chemical laboratories and has led to many traditional analytical procedures being discarded. The GC process can be sensitive enough to detect minute quantities of pesticides in animal tissues and to differentiate between the multiplicity of components in crude oil, as well as complex mixtures of illegal drugs[16]. Because it is sensitive to very small quantities of chemicals and can be totally specific, the procedure has also been applied to determine the amount of alcohol in samples of blood and urine. Almost all analysts now use the method for this purpose in preference to the rather more laborious chemical techniques. It has the added advantage that it requires much less time to train people to use gas chromatographic equipment than to teach them how to obtain accurate results by the chemical methods.

Gas chromatography is really a form of obstacle course for molecules based upon the various physical and chemical properties of the compounds in the sample. In its simplest form, the apparatus consists of a coil of glass tube about 4–6 feet long packed with a granular substance that might consist of anything from powdered brick to synthetic polymeric materials. In some forms of gas chromatography the powder is also used as a support medium for a thick, viscous, non-volatile liquid such as a silicone oil. A continuous flow of gas, usually a mixture of hydrogen and helium or nitrogen, is passed through the column from one end to the other, with the rate of flow carefully regulated by flow meters.

For the analysis of volatile mixtures only minute quantities of the order of 1–2 microlitres (1 millionth part of a litre) are required. Measurement of these small sample volumes is achieved by a specially constructed syringe and the precise quantity is injected into the gas flow at the end of the column. By this means the mixture is carried through the adsorbing material packed inside the column. Due to the physical and chemical differences that exist between the molecular species, they move along the column at different rates and what was originally a mixture is separated into the discrete molecular components. Small unreactive molecules tend to move much faster than do larger reactive substances. As the hydrogen and helium or nitrogen carrier gas leaves the column, it passes through a detector system in which the hydrogen and sample components are identified as a result of the change in electrical signal produced when the gas is burnt at a small jet electrode.

This detector gives a constant reading only while the pure carrier gas passes through, but the reading changes whenever one of the components of the sample mixture is carried out of the column. The detector is linked to a pen recorder which automatically shows the appearance of individual components as a series of peaks traced on a moving roll of chart paper. The sizes of the peaks on the chart are proportional to the relative amounts of each component in the mixture originally injected on to the column. The actual amount present in the sample can be determined by comparison of any peak with a series of standards previously studied.

By operating the gas chromatographic column under carefully controlled conditions, with a steady gas flow, any particular chemical compound will always take the same time to pass through the column. This period, referred to as the 'retention time', is used as the basis for identifying compounds in different mixtures. In practice, the retention times for chemical compounds are established using pure materials and afterwards used for the purpose of identifying the components in mixtures. As the peak area is directly related to the amount of the compound in the sample applied to the column it is, therefore, possible to establish both the identity and the amount of any volatile substance in a solution, as in the case of alcohol in blood or urine.

The block diagram (Figure 22) shows the arrangement of a gas chromatograph and the type of chart record obtained.

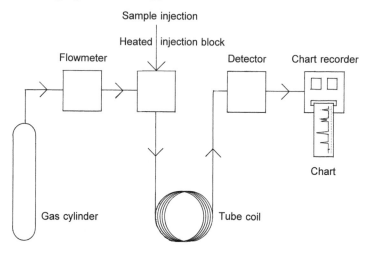

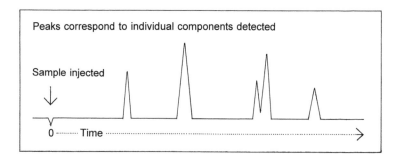

Figure 22 – Block diagram of gas chromatographic equipment used for the analysis of blood and urine samples, and the chart record produced.

Several different approaches to the operation of the instrument exist and there are different techniques for treating the sample prior to injection in the gas flow. As urine samples are almost completely volatile, it is possible to inject them directly on to the head of the column. In the case of blood, however, direct injection of the sample can, after a time, lead to blockage of the head of the column due to the accumulation of non-volatile residues. Because of this, the alcohol in the blood samples is often transferred to a more suitable medium by extraction with another solvent before being injected on to the column. However, for high quality forensic work, both blood and urine samples are analysed by fully automated procedures using what is known as the 'head space' technique[17]. For this purpose, rubber-capped bottles containing measured volumes of the sample are kept at 80–85°C (176–185°F) to vaporise some of the alcohol into the free space above the blood or urine. The sample volume required for the gas chromatography is then extracted from the vapour (the head space) rather than from the liquid so that no solid substances are deposited on the column.

To improve the accuracy of gas chromatographic results even further, analysts make use of a technique[18] involving the addition of another chemical, such as propanol, to the sample under examination. By this means, the amount of ethanol can be assessed by relating the size of its chart peak to the corresponding peak size obtained from the known amount of the 'internal standard'. Any instrumental variations occur to both peaks and cancel out in the method of calculation for the blood alcohol concentration.

An analysis by gas chromatography can take about 30 minutes to carry out and the procedure has the added advantage that it can be fairly easily automated so that a large number of samples can be dealt with in a short space of time. A very high level of accuracy is attained by using experienced technicians and employing instruments used exclusively for the purpose.

Accuracy of analysis

Gas chromatography is considered to be by far the most

desirable method for the analysis of samples containing alcohol as the range of error should not exceed ±3%, and by the use of internal standards it is possible to improve the accuracy to better than ±2%. However, all analytical procedures have an inherent degree of error and allowance must always be made for this before publishing the results. In order to allow for any lack of precision in the analytical methods, the actual figure presented by the prosecution in Great Britain is expressed as a value of "not less than .... milligrams of alcohol in one hundred millilitres of blood/urine". The value recorded on the analytical certificate is a figure obtained after 6 mg (or 6% for values above 100 mg) have been subtracted from the average value obtained in the analyses carried out. It means that a blood sample that on analysis gives an average value of, say, 97 mg, will actually be presented as being 'not less than 91 mg of alcohol in 100 mL of blood'. It also means that this subtraction works to the motorist's advantage because, if the average analytical value is between 81 and 86 mg, then no prosecution for being above the legal limit is likely as subtraction of the 6 mg allowance will produce values below the 81 mg prosecution minimum value.

It is very rare for there to be any major conflict between blood alcohol values obtained by forensic science laboratories and those found by independent analysts. This lack of conflict is very encouraging as the private results will at the least reassure the public that the very techniques which exist to detect the law breaker are also available to protect the innocent.

To assist any driver who seeks an independent analysis of a blood or urine sample for which he may have opted following a positive evidential breath test result, the Royal Society of Chemistry in the UK publishes a list of recognised analytical chemists who have the necessary equipment to undertake analyses, usually by gas chromatography. A copy of this list is normally provided to motorists by the police after a blood or urine sample has been provided.

Chapter 8

THE LEGAL ASPECTS OF DRINK-DRIVING

"Keep ye the Law – be swift in all obedience –
Clear the land of evil, drive the road and bridge the ford.
Make ye sure to each his own.
That he reap where he hath sown
By the peace among our people let men know we serve the Lord!"

Rudyard Kipling

Despite claims that the public love affair with the motor car is over, there is no real indication in any country that people are less prepared to drive both short and long distances or willing to forego the costs and supposed pleasures of owning a vehicle. Many of those who complain about pollution, congestion and the construction of by-passes and motorways are only too prepared to get into their cars to drive to the nearest supermarket or shopping centre.

Very few laws impinge so directly on so many people as do those relating to motoring, the maintenance of vehicles and the ability to control a car on the road. Many people go through life without breaking a single law or committing any offence except those that relate to parking in restricted areas, exceeding the speed limit or driving a car with faulty lamps. The general increase in the mobility of a population due to car ownership leads automatically to an increase in law breaking and a greater proportion of the public appearing in court as offenders. The drink-drive laws have inevitably added to the workload of the courts and to the numbers of those who have been banned from driving for long periods of time.

The introduction of such laws has frequently led to administrative difficulties and created enormous volumes of case law throughout the world. In some instances, such as in the Republic of Ireland in 1978, the problems have become so complicated that the laws have been virtually suspended for a time. The re-writing of drink-drive laws has become a major preoccupation in many countries and states, often because initial drafting of laws has been faulty and numerous legal loopholes have been created.

Saving the driving licence

The desire of motorists to retain their licences to drive is so great that they will frequently resort to considerable expense and the wildest legal subterfuge in order to confound the laws. In the USA, the first law permitting chemical tests was passed in the state of Indiana in 1939 and led to attempts in 1944 to write a similar model law suitable for all the states to use. However, enactment of this law in many states resulted in the increased pleading of the fifth amendment against self-incrimination by the provision of blood samples for analysis. To overcome this problem further legislation was necessary and, in 1953, New York State introduced the first 'implied consent' law in which it said "any person who operates a motor vehicle or motor cycle in this state shall be deemed to have given his consent to a chemical test .... for the purpose of determining the alcoholic content of his blood ...."

Similar legislation in other states[1] managed to overcome the self-incrimination argument but did not deal with the whole myriad of objections based upon the accuracy of the analytical method, the purity of the chemicals, the ability of the police officers or the qualifications of the person taking the sample. With more than forty years' average experience behind the individual state drink-drive laws, most of the loopholes in the USA have been closed by further legislation and case law. But the implied consent aspect remains as a major feature along with an administrative per se law permitting a state to suspend a driving licence based on a blood alcohol concentration or other appropriate criteria[2].

Most of the results and weaknesses which became obvious in the USA should, however, have served as a warning to later legislators in Europe and in other countries. What became quite clear was that legislating on matters involving medical and scientific data is very difficult because science is not absolute but based upon experimental results which may be overthrown at a later date.

In Great Britain very little consideration appeared to have been given to the experiences of other countries following the introduction of their breath test laws and, as a result, similar weaknesses and loopholes were created in the laws enacted by the British Parliament.

For many years, numerous British local by-laws dealt with the offender who was 'drunk and incapable' and it was not until Parliament passed the Licensing Act 1872 that it became an offence to be found drunk in charge of carriages, horses, cattle and steam engines. But the introduction of similar legislation specifically aimed at drivers of motor vehicles was unnecessary for many years since the development of the motor car in Britain was impeded due to the 'Red Flag Act' which had been aimed at protecting pedestrians and horse-drawn vehicles. As a result, it was not until the Criminal Justice Act 1925 that it became an offence to be found 'drunk in charge of any mechanically driven vehicle'. Failure to define what was meant by 'drunk in charge' made interpretation of the law difficult and led very quickly to the Road Traffic Act 1930 in which the offence was rephrased as being 'under the influence of drink or drug to such an extent as to be incapable of having proper control of a vehicle'. Successful prosecutions under this law depended greatly upon the subjective tests and observations of the, then named, police surgeons.

Despite the obvious weaknesses that existed in the absence of objective methods of testing, this law remained in force for thirty years, during which time the British public learnt of stricter laws and scientific assessments being established in Norway, Sweden and Germany. The Road Traffic Act 1960 was eventually introduced to increase penalties which could be imposed for cases of drunken driving; but it was not until the Road Traffic Act 1962 (known as the Marples Act, after the then Minister of Transport), that the first approaches to using blood or urine samples for establishing blood alcohol levels were made. It was also this Act of Parliament which made it an offence if "the ability to drive properly is for the time being impaired". Thus, for the first time in Britain the law recognised that it was not necessary for people to be totally incapable of driving because of alcohol for them to be a danger on the roads.

This particular Act did not make it compulsory for an accused motorist to supply a sample of blood or urine when asked to do so by a police constable but it did establish that refusal to consent to provide a sample could be used as supporting evidence for the prosecution concerning his condition at the time. It also laid down the procedures to be followed in obtaining, dividing, supplying and analysing the specimens of blood or urine. It is not generally known that the 1962 Act also contained the first mention of the possibility of the police asking for breath samples for analysis. At that time no figures for the relationship between alcohol in blood, urine and breath were defined and no apparatus for taking breath samples had been approved, although there was ample knowledge available at the time for all of these to have been dealt with.

The breath test law

Following the deliberations of more committees, further studies and additional reports, the British Government eventually felt that the road accident figures were serious enough to justify tighter restrictions on drinking and driving. As a result, the later Road Safety Act 1967, which was piloted through Parliament by Barbara Castle, built upon the earlier Act and led to the introduction of roadside breath tests and the establishment of the legal blood alcohol limit at 80 mg of alcohol per 100 mL of blood[3]. However, the earlier 1962 Act was not repealed and drivers with alcohol in their blood could still be charged under the earlier Act if it could be shown that driving ability had been impaired through taking alcohol or other drugs, or for being drunk in charge of a motor vehicle. The Act made no effort to define the form of apparatus the police could use for the breath test, although it did say it had to be of a type approved by the Secretary of State.

It was not intended that any conviction for being above the legal limit could be made solely on the basis of a positive result from a breath test. Such a result was only intended as a justification for the police to demand a blood or urine sample for a laboratory investigation.

Consolidation of the various Acts covering drink-driving later took place under the Road Traffic Act 1972.

Legal loopholes

The Road Safety Act 1967 was far from being a water-tight document and at one time it was claimed that at least 50 technical loopholes existed in the eight pages of that Act of Parliament which covered the breath test and legal limits. Over the following five years most of those loopholes were tested in court, so that by the time the law was updated[4] by the Road Traffic Act 1972, many of the gaps had been closed by case law.

However, despite the added strength of the Road Traffic Act 1972 and the closing of loopholes[5], defended prosecutions and appeals against convictions continued to occupy considerable court time. Criticisms of many aspects of the roadside screening test and the problems associated with enforcing the law also occurred. The police found particular difficulties in bringing prosecutions in cases in which the offender managed to drink a further amount of, usually, whisky or brandy after an accident or after evading arrest and before being detained. This became known as the 'hip-flask' defence and generally meant that any later blood sample result was totally invalid. Problems also arose in those instances in which a motorist managed to reach home and get inside his house before the police could catch up with him. This loophole had only been partially blocked in 1970 as a result of the case of John F Jones of Breconshire[6], in which the Appeal Court Judge, Lord Justice Sachs, stated that "It is not in the view of this court of law that a motorist, merely by turning off a highway, can stultify police action and escape being required to give a breath test, when action would otherwise be proper."

In this particular instance, the driver had been stopped after turning into his own driveway, so it was considered to constitute a different set of circumstances from those which applied when a motorist had stopped his car, alighted and actually entered his house.

Thus the situation in which a motorist was traced to his home address following a minor collision and breath tested while in bed, invalidated the test on a variety of grounds. What it did do was to confirm the view[7] that drivers who had been drinking had less to lose in terms of fines and bans if they drove off after an accident than if they stayed and faced a drink-drive charge. This led to an increase of more than 50% (from 12,000 to 18,000) in only seven years in the number of convictions for motorists failing to stop after an accident.

Weaknesses of this type that remained in the law and developments in the field of electronic measuring devices for breath alcohol quickly led the British Government to decide to reassess the whole of the operation and efficacy of the drink-drive laws and their enforcement.

Blennerhassett Report

Although regular reviews of drink-drive legislation are common features in motoring countries, there is no doubt that the post-legislation study carried out in Great Britain was one of the most detailed. What became known as the Blennerhassett Committee was set up in June 1974 and, after many delays and leaks to the press, published its report in February 1976. The committee and its legal sub-committee had a total of 18 meetings and considered evidence from 35 organisations and 57 individuals. However, despite its survey of the results of the earlier legislation and its proposals for changes in the law, its impact was that of a soggy sponge. For many months the British Government failed to act upon its recommendations and when it did it was in a half-hearted, lukewarm manner.

The Blennerhassett recommendations[8] fell into three main areas:

1. Those related to aspects of the current law (the Road Traffic Act 1972).

2. Those concerned with high risk offenders.

3. Those concerned with publicity and young offenders.

As regards the established legislation, it was proposed to continue with an 80 mg limit, to press for the introduction of alternative roadside screening devices to the Alcotest 80, and for the use of evidential breath tests at the police station with blood samples only as an option.

The report singled out 'high-risk' offenders as those convicted twice for drinking and driving in ten years and estimated that they would comprise at least 10% of all offenders within a few years. A 'high-risk' category was proposed as applying to anyone with a blood alcohol level over 200 mg and the recommendation was made that such a person, in addition to normal penalties, should not be entitled to regain his driving licence unless he could satisfy the court that his drinking habits did not make him an 'undue' danger on the roads.

Major parts of the report showed concern about the education of young drivers and recommended that research on drink and drugs in relation to driving should be a high priority. It also made the very strong point that publicity should not be spasmodic and restricted to public holidays such as the Christmas period, but continuous and authoritative.

Despite all these strong views, there were severe weaknesses and omissions in the report[9] and a general lack of feeling that anything would be done immediately.

The greatest weakness was in the failure to recommend reducing the legal limit to 50 mg. The continued acceptance of the 80 mg limit was on the basis that a lower limit would broaden the field of offenders (as it obviously would), although some people also argue that very few additional motorists would be caught in the 50–80 mg region. Whichever is correct, they all ignore the fact that it is above the 50 mg level that the accident potential really starts to climb, that having an 80 mg limit is an encouragement to drink to that level and that the introduction of a 50 mg limit should have a similarly salutary effect as the 80 mg limit had when originally introduced. The Blennerhassett adherence to the 80 mg limit was made in the face of its own comments about motorists being "unable to react fast enough to unforeseen hazards .... at blood alcohol concentrations as low as 40 mg/100 mL" obtained from a Swedish demonstration. As it is, there is a progressive downward trend in acceptable blood alcohol levels in countries throughout the motoring world and, over the next ten years, 50 mg levels will become increasingly more common.

Another omission of the report was its failure to face up to the reality that drunken pedestrians, cyclists and horse riders also cause accidents. Even now it is still common in most countries for a sober motorist to have to submit to a breath test while a drunken pedestrian or cyclist does not. Despite this anomaly and the number of killed cyclists having high blood alcohol levels, no suggestion was made that there should be any change in this aspect of the law.

Although enormous publicity was given to the Blennerhassett recommendations, the introduction of any legislation based upon it was continuously delayed until after the General Election of 1979 when the new Conservative government issued a consultative document[10] covering the points that it was felt needed to be considered and the possible approaches that might be made with a new drink-drive law. Many of those who replied[11,12] to the consultative document, including this author, supported the introduction of evidential breath testing, the retention of the blood sample option and, in some cases, advocated the lowering of the legal blood alcohol limit.

The 1981 Act

With consultations still proceeding following the publication of the Blennerhassett report, tests and field trials were also carried out on improved screening and evidential breath testing instruments. Eventually, the committees, consultations and discussions led to the British Parliament passing the Transport Act 1981[13] in which section 25 replaced sections 6–

12 of the Road Traffic Act 1972. However, implementation of section 25 of the 1981 Act introducing evidential breath testing did not take place until 6 May 1983. This was mainly due to the extended trials on evidential breath testing machines and the need for the manufacturers to make, test and check the large number of instruments required for the police and to train operators before evidential breath testing could be established.

The 1981 Act retained most of the 1972 legislation but gave the police much greater flexibility over the procedure to be followed in the roadside screening test[14]. At the same time, it limited the scope for the provision of blood and urine samples by a motorist, with the attendant time delays and, as far as possible, substituted them with evidential breath samples, which had already been in use in Northern Ireland[15] since 1968.

The 1981 Act also retained the legal limits of 80 mg for blood and 107 mg for urine but for the first time introduced the legal limit of 35 µg for alcohol in the breath. The establishment of a specific limit in breath overcame any problems about converting breath alcohol values to blood alcohol levels, although the correlation of the two is of importance in connection with the accuracy and efficiency of evidential breath testing instruments. The Secretary of State still has powers to alter these levels by regulations if wished, but no intention of introducing lower levels was indicated then or has been since.

Previously, case law following the 1967 Act had established that the police had to be in uniform and to rigorously carry out the specified procedure relating to the screening test for the result to be valid and to justify arresting a motorist in order to request a blood sample. The 1981 Act meant that it was no longer necessary to show that the procedural requirements for the roadside test and the arrest had been complied with. It enabled a constable to "arrest a person without warrant if he has reasonable cause to suspect that person is or has been committing an offence", and added "a constable may enter (if need by force) any place where the person is". These clauses alone closed many of the bases for arguing in court that screening tests had been incorrectly or improperly carried out. The Act also extended the scope under which police could ask for a breath test and it became an offence for a person to refuse to provide a breath sample even if it was later shown that he or she was not at that time the driver of a motor vehicle or intending to drive.

Evidential tests

Because the Act introduced evidential breath testing for the first time, it also entitled any person recording breath alcohol values of 50 μg or less to have the option of providing a blood or urine sample (whichever is specified by the police officer). Many people involved with the drink-drive laws believed that the greatest weakness in the 1981 Act, particularly in view of the introduction of evidential breath testing, was the removal of the right for *all* offenders to provide a blood sample for laboratory analysis. The previous 1967 and 1972 Acts had established the right of a motorist to have a proportion of his sample of blood or urine upon which he could obtain a private confirmatory analysis if he desired. As a consequence of the 1981 Act, the majority of motorists lost a right which had been clearly established for more than 14 years. It was obviously a retrograde step that led to a great lack of confidence in the integrity of the results coming from the evidential breath testing machines. Had the 1981 Act continued to provide for all motorists to have the right to ask for a blood sample following a positive evidential breath sample, there is no doubt that within a short space of time the numbers asking for the option would have dropped to levels below 10%, as in other countries. The non-provision of the blood option, except in marginal cases, automatically led to many stories (often repeated by newspapers without adequate checking) that "I only had two pints of lager and the machine gave a false value of 60 μg."

As a consequence, the whole of the post-1983 evidential breath testing campaign ran into considerable difficulties and led to a major newspaper campaign against the equipment employed for this purpose. Many of the stories carried during the campaign were highly subjective and often lacked proper verification, but for a time undermined public confidence in Great Britain in the evidential breath testing process. However, by April 1984, the British Government decided to restore the right to a blood sample to all motorists, as a temporary measure, to enable further Home Office investigations and checks to be carried out.

This was originally intended to be for a trial period of only six months but was further extended in October 1984 in order that various bodies and committees could report on the reliability of breath alcohol readings in comparison with corresponding blood samples. The one interesting fact that immediately came out from this was that, right from the start, only about one-third of the motorists took up the blood option, the remainder being quite prepared to accept the results from the evidential breath testing instruments. Also, as had been predicted, by the beginning of 1985 the proportion requesting blood samples had dropped very rapidly to levels of between 10 and 20% in many police districts. Home Office results[16] comparing blood and breath alcohol levels on dual samples taken since the introduction of evidential breath testing in 1983 showed very good correlation between the two fluids based upon average values for the time correction necessary between the taking of the two sets of samples. Similar close relationships have been found in other recent surveys that have been carried out and the indication is that, by taking the lower of the two breath alcohol values for prosecution purposes, in the majority of cases the breath value will be lower than the corresponding blood alcohol level.

Evidential breath tests cleared

The Home Office report[17] on evidential breath alcohol measuring devices, covering the period 16 April 1984 – 15 October 1984, was the most extensive survey of the type ever carried out anywhere in the world. Altogether, 12,066 blood (or urine) and breath comparisons were made. The report showed quite clearly that people were not being falsely convicted on the basis of evidential breath testing machines and, if anything, the breath alcohol results obtained were operating to the benefit of motorists rather than against them. These results were supported by a similar but smaller study carried out simultaneously by the Royal Society of Chemistry[18]. Because of the level of public concern previously engendered over acetone detection and over any large differences between the two breath alcohol values, it was decided that the automatic police power to request blood samples should be extended to these doubtful areas and the period for the general blood option would be extended for at least a further 12 months. By these means, almost all the contentious areas on evidential breath testing were dealt with effectively in one go and more than justified earlier criticisms made by specialists in this area.

Breath test defences

The lack of flexibility enjoyed by the police in being able to allow the motorist the right to have a blood sample taken also meant that any apparent errors, mistakes, malfunctions or breakdowns in the breath testing machines led to hundreds of claims that the results were invalid or falsely inflated. Following the introduction of the Lion Intoximeter 3000 and the Camic Breath Analyser into British police stations, it soon became clear that the inflexibility over the blood options was producing defences based upon four main contentions. These were:

1. "I was unable to provide a sample, not because of lack of co-operation but because it was impossible to blow into the machine due to resistance in the tube" or "because I do not have enough lung capacity."

2. "The two results recorded for my two breath samples differ by a wide margin and indicate that the machine was faulty at the time of the test."

3. "My printout from the Lion Intoximeter showed that I have acetone in my breath, but I am not a diabetic so the machine must be faulty and the results incorrect." The converse of this is "I am a diabetic but the machine has not shown the presence of acetone so it must be faulty."

4. "My high breath alcohol results are due to solvents which I have absorbed, swallowed or inhaled and are being blown out in my breath."

It must be stated that the vast majority of these claims were spurious and without substance in any way and successful defences against evidential breath alcohol results in Great Britain were, and are, few and far between. But had the blood option existed right from the start, none of them need have arisen at all and evidential breath testing would have been accepted by the British public with no great problem and a great deal of police and court time and money would have been saved. It was the fact that there was no way the sceptical motorist could obtain an independent analysis that eventually led to the enormous controversy on radio, television and in the national newspapers.

Breath sampling and samples

The most common reason for failing to provide a breath sample is, in fact, evasive blowing with the subject blowing around the mouthpiece rather than down it, or by sucking back during the process of blowing. True medical or physical reasons for failing to provide a sample are relatively uncommon. Similarly, the most common reasons for variations between the two samples relate more to the subject rather than to the machines and depend upon how hard the person actually blows when providing the samples and how they breathe in between samples. However, where really large differences do occur between the two recorded values, each set of results needs to be studied on its merits and this is one area in which the blood option should be automatic. The Paton Report[17] recommended that where the two breath results differed by 20% there should be automatic recourse to blood samples. However, this has never been officially implemented but recommendations for third generation instruments[19], issued in 1994, specify separation "by no more than 15% of the lower reading".

The recording of acetone levels on the Lion Intoximeter 3000 has actually been a red herring in the sense that the secondary acetone detector is more likely to over-compensate, producing a low breath alcohol value rather than a high one, to the advantage of the motorist. Defended cases based upon inhaled and absorbed solvents are also rarely successful because the quantities involved often mean that, to produce the recorded 'apparent' alcohol values, the subject would have had to have been exposed to lethal atmospheres for several hours and would have exhibited far worse symptoms than those just associated with being above the legal alcohol limit. A close examination of the background to such claims is usually sufficient to show that they lack any real merit, although there are some occasions in which such solvents could have a marginal effect on recorded alcohol values obtained immediately after exposure to solvents has ceased.

On-site investigations in polluted car spraying and French polishing workshops have shown[20] that, in general, the solvent atmosphere only produces artificial breath alcohol values for a short time after exposure ceases. There is generally no long-term retention effect due to inhaled or absorbed solvents.

The operation of the legislation

One important change that was first made by the introduction of the 1967 Act was that the offence of driving or attempting to drive with blood alcohol level in excess of the prescribed limit was absolute. Drivers could no longer call their own medical doctor to give evidence that they were sober. Detained drivers could only ask for their own doctor to be called in the event of injury or illness, but not for the purpose of ascertaining if they were sober or to delay the tests. They did, however, have to pay the fee of the doctor called to take the blood sample if they were eventually found guilty of being over the legal limit.

Blood samples must only be taken by a Forensic Medical Examiner who is also required to sign a certificate stating that the sample was taken with the consent of the driver.

As things stand, the law does not define the parts of the anatomy from which blood samples may be taken. At one time this produced an escape for a number of motorists who created almost impossible situations by offering sensitive parts of their anatomy as the sample site. These gaps in the law were closed within a few years of the introduction of the 1967 Act. In a case in Manchester, the magistrates ruled that a police surgeon was correct in refusing to take a blood sample from a motorist's foot, and in North London a driver was found guilty of failing to supply a sample after asking the doctor to take it from his penis. For the subject to try and lay down conditions for his co-operation is now considered to be a refusal and therefore a 'failure to provide a sample'.

It should be pointed out that the 1967 Road Safety Act did not provide for the driver to be given a portion of his blood or urine sample in order to have a private analysis carried out, although this right had previously existed for people stopped under the 1962 Road Traffic Act. The omission was not rectified until the later Road Traffic Act 1972 was introduced and the right was retained in the 1981 and subsequent Acts of Parliament. During the five-year period 1967–72, most motorists were, in fact, given the opportunity to have a portion of the sample they had provided but there were many instances of them not being adequately informed on how to store the sample or how to go about obtaining a private analysis. Fortunately, this is now a thing of the past and motorists are more than protected against their own ignorance.

Although the method of sealing and storing samples is not laid down by any law, the containers and procedure used (described in Chapter 7) have evolved after many years of experience and several court cases involving arguments on the admissibility of evidence obtained after incorrect sampling procedures, poor sample containers or poor storage conditions. Police evidence on blood samples has been held to be inadmissible in cases in which the driver was supplied with a sample that was too small for a private analysis to be made. A similar ruling has been made in which the private analysis sample has clotted or dried in the sample tube. This is an important point as it suggests that the driver must have the same opportunity as the police to assess the blood alcohol level; that is, the sample provided to the driver must be one that is capable of analysis (*Earl v Roy*

[1969] 2 ALL ER 684). If it is not, then the Act has not been complied with[21].

Urine samples do not, of course, require recourse to syringes but in these cases two samples within a one-hour period are required by the police. This is because the first sample is disregarded as its main purpose is to clear the bladder completely to enable the urine in equilibrium with the blood to be obtained for the second sample. An adequate portion of the urine sample must also be offered to the driver to enable a private analysis to be carried out.

Where police analysts and private analysts have produced conflicting results, with the former being above the prescribed limit and the latter below, magistrates have sometimes, although not invariably, found the accused not guilty because of contradictory evidence. In some instances, the Crown Prosecution Service drops the charges before they come to court.

In cases in which the driver has been involved in an accident and taken to hospital, the police are not entitled to make any tests or take any samples without the consent of the medical practitioner in charge of the patient. Refusal of permission can be made by the medical practitioner in those cases in which he considers it could undermine the treatment of the patient.

Further developments in the law

As a result of further drink-drive court cases which threatened to open additional legal loopholes for drivers to slip through, a further consolidation of laws and decisions was made under the Road Traffic Act 1988, linked with the Road Traffic Offenders Act 1988 and the Road Traffic (Consequential Provisions) Act 1988. However, there still appears to be plenty of scope for lawyers to find possible ways of saving defendants' driving licences[22,23]. It is, in any case, important to appreciate that whilst the various drink-drive Acts have gone some way to restoring the balance towards safer driving and law enforcement, they still maintain the essential safeguards needed for drivers and motorcyclists to receive fair treatment by well established processes. These can be summarised as follows:

(a) Requests for roadside breath tests can only come from a uniformed police officer.

(b) Tests must be carried out with apparatus that has been approved for this purpose by the Home Secretary.

(c) No patient in hospital can be asked to take a test without the consent of the medical practitioner in charge.

(d) An evidential breath test or request for a blood or urine sample can only be made if the roadside screening has indicated that the driver is (i) above the prescribed limit, (ii) has failed to take the screening test, or (iii) if the police have reasonable cause to believe that a drink-drive offence has been committed.

(e) The custody officer at the police station will request two breath samples to be provided on an approved evidential breath testing machine. A blood (or, rarely, a urine) sample will only be asked for if no machine is available or if it is believed that there is some medical reason why the motorist is unable to provide suitable breath samples for the machine to analyse.

(f) A motorist with a breath alcohol value between 35 µg and 50 µg (in practice between 40 µg and 50 µg as prosecution does not usually occur on values of 39 µg and less due to potential machine variations) shall be given the option to choose to have the results replaced by values obtained from the analysis of a blood or urine sample.

(g) The accused motorist must be provided with a copy of any analytical certificate at least seven days before any court hearing. In the case of an evidential breath test, a copy of the machine printout must be offered after the test has been completed.

(h) Persons required to provide a breath sample (or, if necessary, a blood or urine sample) must be warned in advance that refusal to supply the sample will make them liable to being charged as if they were over the legal limit. Failure by the police to give this warning can lead to any charge being dismissed.

(i) A blood sample can only be taken by a qualified medical practitioner and then only with the consent of the person concerned.

(j) If blood or urine samples are applicable, the motorist must be asked which is preferred, although the police officer may decide which fluid should be supplied.

(k) The person supplying a blood or urine sample is entitled to retain a sealed portion of the sample for a private analysis to be carried out.

Penalties for driving or attempting to drive with excess alcohol are also becoming heavier. They now consist of a fine of up to £2000, loss of driving licence for a minimum of one year and a maximum of three years, plus possible imprisonment for up to six months. In practice, magistrates make reference to guidelines for penalties for first offences, roughly in proportion to the breath or blood alcohol level.

It should be emphasised that magistrates in Great Britain now have very little discretion on the penalties they impose on the 'over-the-limit' driver. Disqualification is automatic and can now only be waived in very exceptional circumstances. For these to apply, it is necessary for the extenuating circumstances to be directly connected with the offence. It is not, for instance, sufficient that the accused is a professional driver, needs to drive to earn a living or provides a public service through driving. However, a sudden emergency causing the person to drive when they would not normally have driven and when alternative transport was unavailable could come into this category.

As a result of the Road Traffic Act 1991, a compulsory prison sentence is now imposed on drivers causing death when driving under the influence of alcohol or drugs, with the maximum period of detention being five years.

For motorists classified as 'high-risk' offenders, special

measures now apply. If convicted of drink/driving twice within ten years or recorded as providing blood samples with alcohol levels exceeding 200 mg (87 µg in breath), they are required to obtain counselling during their disqualification for any drinking problems. Before the end of their three year period of ban, they are informed that the return of their licence will be subject to a special medical examination and proof that any alcohol problems have been overcome. It is, of course, essential that such high-risk drivers and recidivists are provided with the help and guidance they require.

'Hip flask' and 'laced drink' defences

As a result of the strengthened drink-drive laws, the vast majority of drink-drive prosecutions are successful, with accused motorists usually pleading guilty to the charges. Unsuccessful prosecutions, when they occur, are often due to incorrect procedures being followed at the police station. However, there are two successful approaches which enable drivers to save their licences. These are:

1. The post-driving drinks defence – commonly known as the 'hip-flask' defence.

2. The laced drinks or substituted drinks 'special reasons' plea.

The post-driving drinks defence is frequently presented by people who have driven off after being involved in an accident and who claim to have drunk large quantities, usually of spirits, before being arrested. This excuse is actually written into British law which specifically says that, if it can be shown by the defence that a motorist drank alcohol after an accident that was responsible for putting him or her over the legal limit when tested, then that may be considered reasonable grounds not to be convicted. However, the onus is entirely on the motorist to prove that, but for any drinks taken after the incident for which he was tested, he would not have been above the legal limit.

In many cases a defence is attempted simply based upon the claim that the motorist has later drunk an ill-defined amount of vodka or whisky which is held responsible for putting them above the legal limit when tested. However, for a defence of this type to stand any real chance of success it has to satisfy much tighter criteria than this[24]. Not only must the post-incident drinking account for the breath or blood alcohol level in excess of the legal limit, it is also necessary for the person's total stated alcohol consumption to account fully for the recorded breath or blood alcohol level, after allowing for alcohol eliminated from the body and to show by means of a back calculation that the driver was below the legal limit when the accident occurred. In addition to this, it is essential that the police are notified of the nature and extent of the post-accident drinking as soon as possible. It is because many defences in this category do not meet these criteria that they are generally unsuccessful in court.

The laced drinks 'special reasons' pleas have to satisfy similar criteria, although in these cases the defendants plead guilty to the drink-drive charge but claim they were not responsible for being over the legal limit as they had unknowingly drunk extra alcohol with which their drinks had been 'laced' (spiked with spirits). It is usually claimed that the lacing was carried out using vodka when their backs were turned or they were visiting the toilet.

In the majority of cases, the plea is unsuccessful due to the failure of the person who has added the vodka either to give evidence or to be able to quantify the amount of vodka that might have been added. There is no doubt that a large number of these 'special reasons' pleas are totally fabricated and this usually becomes very evident once the calculations have been carried out or the evidence of supporting witnesses is heard in court.

Variations on the laced drinks pleas are pleas based upon claims that the motorist has inadvertently exceeded the legal limit due to taking a medicine or tonic containing alcohol or being given a normal strength beer or lager instead of a low alcohol drink as expected. In all of these cases the big weakness is always in the claim that the driver was unaware that they were above the legal limit when they were driving. As has been pointed out elsewhere (page 35), a person has to be very seriously intoxicated to still be above the legal limit when the analytical samples are taken. This is especially the case in states and countries which are still operating legal limits of 100 mg.

Genuine defences and pleas in these categories are usually quite obvious and calculations for the alcohol levels based on the amount drunk normally correspond very well with those actually measured, despite the variations, tolerances and conversion factors that have to be applied.

Back calculations in hip flask and laced drinks defences are very common and a number of successful claims have been made in the British courts. However, a large number of factors have to be taken into consideration, including the volume and nature of the drinks consumed, the time period over which they are drunk and the weight and sex of the subject.

Unfortunately, despite the attempts of the various Acts to reduce the number of hip flask defences, they have in fact drawn attention to this approach as being a valid line to take. As a result, there has been an enormous increase in the number of motorists seeking expert calculations based upon the 'fact' that they drank, for example, two large double brandies or half a bottle of whisky due to shock after being involved in an accident.

Despite the fairly common occurrence of these back calculations for defence purposes, members of the medical and legal professions in Britain became very agitated in June 1986 when exactly the same process was used successfully by the prosecution to obtain a conviction in the Magistrates' Court in Birmingham. In this case, the motorist had been involved in a car accident in which a man had been killed. The police had been unable to obtain a blood sample from the driver until 4 hours and 20 minutes after the accident as he had been taken to hospital. Even after that great length of time, it still produced an analysis value of 'not less than 59 milligrams per 100 millilitres of blood'. It was accepted by the court that that level was sufficient to show that the driver must have been above the legal limit of 80 mg at the time of the accident.

This case, which created a new precedent in British law, has had very important consequences, as it showed that so long as continuity of supervision of the motorist is maintained after the accident and no additional alcohol is consumed, a driver is not necessarily 'not guilty' just because the eventual analytical results are below the legal limit.

No random tests

It should be emphasised that the drink-drive laws in Great Britain do not permit the police to carry out random roadside breath tests, although a number of Chief Constables and outside bodies have been requesting these for many years. However, they are permitted to stop vehicles for checks on road tax discs and roadworthiness and can test the drivers for alcohol if they have reason to believe they have been drinking. At present, by operating on a discriminatory basis, it means that the police are able to select those drivers who appear most likely to have been drinking.

Although some politicians, police officers and magistrates have said they see no reason why the police should not sit outside public houses ready to stop anybody preparing to drive a car, there are good reasons why this is undesirable. In the first instance, it is a waste of time as the instructions for the use of roadside screening devices state that at least 20 minutes must elapse between the last drink and carrying out the test. As has already been seen, this is because residual mouth alcohol may take 15–20 minutes to disperse after drinking and any test during this period is very likely to produce an artificially high reading. Also, it is likely to give misleading results because the blood alcohol, and hence the corresponding breath alcohol, level is unlikely to have reached an equilibrium state. As a result, any reading on the screening device fails to be a true indication of whether the drinking has put the suspect over the limit.

Lower limits?

Despite nearly 30 years of drink-drive legal limits in Great Britain, successive governments have failed to take steps to lower the levels. Many people and organisations have sought a reduction to a blood alcohol level of 50 mg and the present laws do provide scope for the present legal limits to be changed to "such other proportion as may be prescribed by regulations made by the Secretary of State". So there is nothing permanent or immutable about the present very high and generous levels. Similarly, the Secretary of State is not restricted to limiting the blood sample option only to those motorists with breath alcohol values of 50 μg and below as he may "by regulations substitute another proportion of alcohol in the breath for that (the 50 μg) specified". It is quite clear that the Act does provide sufficient flexibility to enable a dual system of evidential breath testing with blood options to be maintained on a permanent basis without the need to pass a fresh Act of Parliament. This is certainly not a situation in which there is any reason or justification for waiting for unanimity within the European Union or the acquiescence of the motoring organisations. Evidence to warrant the introduction of the lower limit is already overwhelming.

Northern Ireland law

The difference in the law between Great Britain (England, Scotland and Wales) and that in Northern Ireland is not well known, although the Northern Ireland law was introduced in 1968. It differs in that, in addition to the 80 mg level, it classifies anybody above 125 mg as having committed a more serious offence which carries more severe penalties. Northern Ireland is not alone in this two-tier approach to the drinking driver as it is used in several states in the USA as well as in other countries in Europe. It is claimed that the lower limit is aimed at catching the 'social' drinker who has drunk a little too well and the higher limit is aimed at the heavy drinker and the problem drinker.

Motor vehicles only

One of the major weaknesses in drink-drive laws throughout

the world, including the USA and Great Britain, is the way in which the motorist and motorcyclist have been singled out for attention. In almost all cases, roadside screening tests and evidential tests can still only be applied to persons driving or in charge of motor vehicles. Police have no authority to ask cyclists or pedestrians to submit to a breath test or to provide any form of evidential sample. As a result, the law is still weighted against the sober motorist who is involved in an accident with a drunken cyclist or pedestrian. It has been made very clear that the policeman in Great Britain who, under the 1967 Act, made a drunken cyclist take a breath test was exceeding his powers and was leaving himself open to legal proceedings for assault. Under section 19 of the 1972 Act a cyclist can, however, be charged with cycling under the influence of drink or drugs, but this has to be proved by the discredited subjective testing of a Forensic Medical Examiner.

International differences

Considerable differences in drink-drive laws exist throughout the world and attempts at improvement in the nature of the legislation are being made all the time. Credit must be given to New Zealand[25] for being the first country to introduce a legal breath alcohol limit in 1978. At present that country operates a breath alcohol level of 40 µg and a blood alcohol level of 80 mg (based upon a conversion factor of 1:2000). The Federal Government in the USA has been trying to persuade the various states to produce similar drink-drive laws and has been very successful in recent years. The European Union has tried to find a way to interfere with individual member nations' rights in this area but has so far been unable discover a clause in the various treaties that gives it the authority to dictate legal limits.

However, the use of sophisticated electronic equipment for law enforcement is being greatly extended throughout the world and an increasing number of countries are in the process of considering legal limits applied directly to breath alcohol values. They would be well advised to consider the problems that arose in Great Britain due to limiting the blood option before the public had learnt to accept the integrity of the machines, before drafting their own legislation.

Irrespective of the differences now applying, it is clear that there is an international trend to reduce blood alcohol limits to 50 mg and to depend to a greater extent on evidential breath testing. Whilst total unanimity is highly unlikely, co-operation and general agreement in this area of road safety have increased enormously in recent years.

Chapter 9

ALCOHOL AND OTHER ACCIDENTS

"All the crimes on earth do not destroy so many of the human race, nor alienate so much property, as drunkenness."

Francis Bacon

There is no doubt that most of the public concern, political pressure and research regarding alcohol and its effects has been devoted to its involvement in road accidents and to alcoholics or problem drinkers. One consequence of this preoccupation with road casualties has been to distract attention from the equally wide involvement of alcohol with accidents in the home, at work and in leisure activities, although this is now changing.

It is not often appreciated that every day almost as many deaths occur from accidents in the home as on the roads. Research has shown that alcohol is a factor in 32% of home accidents and in 62% of cases in which serious head injuries have been sustained. In addition to this, 40% of people attending accident and emergency units have been drinking[1], and alcohol is implicated in 26% of drownings and 39% of deaths in fires.

The increase in home-brewing of beer and home wine-making means that it is almost impossible to assess the true level of drinking in the home but, when this is accompanied by the use of high-powered lawnmowers, electric saws and drills and other do-it-yourself activities, then the contribution of alcohol to home accidents will also increase.

During recent years, there has been increasing use of biological indicators and red blood cell measurements as a guide to whether or not a person is a heavy consumer of alcohol. In particular, the plasma or serum measurement of γ-glutamyltransferase activity (GGT) is considered to be the

145

most important indicator of excess alcohol intake[2]. This was used as the basis for an investigation[3] into the levels of biological indicators in all accident victims admitted as patients to 21 hospitals in France, including those injured in sports, leisure and home activities. Amongst the additional results of a very detailed survey of nearly 500 casualties, it was shown that men were more likely to be involved in accidents at work than were women and women were more likely to have accidents at home. This difference was to be expected as more women are likely to spend longer hours in the home and men tend to do heavier and more dangerous tasks at work. However, it was found in about 21% of the home casualties that the blood alcohol level exceeded 80 mg and this level was also found in 6% of the work casualties and 3% of the sport casualties. The actual numbers with *some* alcohol in their bodies greatly exceeded these levels and indicated that alcohol was a major contributory factor in these accidents.

Alcohol and the worker

For a number of years there has been increasing concern over the part played by alcohol in industrial accidents[4]. Despite this, many countries do not carry out blood tests on people killed in accidents at work, nor do they make any serious effort to establish the level of involvement of alcohol in the working environment. However, building sites, which have traditionally been considered to be areas of relatively lax controls, are being much more carefully supervised to prevent the drinking builder from endangering his colleagues. For many years in Britain, coal miners have not been allowed to go on shift if it is clear that they have recently been drinking heavily. A number of companies have now introduced optional breath testing as a further safeguard and deterrent against heavy drinkers working in a potentially dangerous environment. One of the first agreements of this type was in the British Steel plant at Clyde Bridge, Glasgow in 1979 but generally this has been found to be a very sensitive industrial relations area and effective control is frequently only limited to restrictions against taking alcohol into the working areas.

In 1980, Williams and Brake in their major work *Drink in Great Britain 1900-1979* stated[5] that "A neglected area of research has been the relation of drinking and accident efficiency at work", and it is true to say that whilst statistics from various countries all clearly show the definite relationship between industrial accidents and alcohol, few in-depth quantitative studies have been carried out. One study in 1960, involving a sample of 5000 workers in Strasbourg, showed that 15% of industrial accidents leading to the stopping of work could be attributed to alcohol[6,7]. It can be safely concluded that excessive drinkers are most likely to be involved in accidents whilst at work and this has been firmly underlined by a survey[8] carried out on people attending at alcohol information centres run by the National Council on Alcoholism in Great Britain. This showed that 91% sometimes drank throughout the day, whilst 12% took a bottle (of alcoholic drink) to work with them *every* day. These very high and alarming figures do relate, of course, to a self-selected group of people, many possessing a drink problem but it is generally acknowledged that there is considerable scope for much more research into studies on accidents and casualties in the home and industrial environment[9].

A major attempt to summarise the then available data was made in 1977 by a working party of the National Council on Alcoholism, chaired by Sir Bernard Braine, MP. The report[10] made horrifying reading, showing that compared with other workers, excessive drinkers not only had five times the number of days off for sickness, but had three times the number of accidents at work. Support was lent to these figures by a study in Scotland[11] which showed that, of 35 industrial fatalities, 20% involved blood alcohol levels in excess of the British legal drink-drive limit of 80 mg.

Of special interest in the context of industrial accidents are the results of a study carried out at the Polytechnic of Wales[12,13], reported in 1980. Studies were made of three different industrial situations with different types of potential hazards for workers. Two of these showed a peak accident period during the two hours after a new shift came on duty. The third (a laboratory) showed a peak accident period during the two hours after the lunch break. It was concluded that alcohol played a major role in the accidents during these periods as a result of workers drinking immediately prior to going on duty or drinking during lunchtime.

The validity of this conclusion was proved by a special test in which volunteers working together in pairs had to carry a two metre hardboard roll filled with sand and metal chips and weighing 20 kilograms, along an L-shaped corridor with specially sensitised walls. Tests were carried out before the volunteers had drunk any alcohol and again after drinking various quantities of alcohol. It was found that increased consumption of alcohol led to more wall collisions per minute. The increase compared with those who had no alcohol in their bodies ranged from twice the number of collisions at a blood alcohol level of 30 mg to five times the number at 80 mg. It is perhaps not unexpected that these results are very similar to those obtained for drinking drivers (Figure 8, page 53).

It does not come as any surprise to learn that the World Health Organisation has estimated that in Europe alcohol-related injuries place a burden of between 5% and 6% on the gross national product[14].

The one conclusion that can be reached from the various reports which have been produced is that low productivity, poor standards of workmanship and high accident rates may all have a direct relationship with drinking prior to and during working hours[15]. It should, however, be emphasised that alcohol is not the only factor that applies and should not be used as an excuse for not carrying out the very necessary safety precautions that are required in the industrial environment.

Alcohol and flying

The safe carriage of passengers is something that has always concerned the air transportation industry, particularly because any accidents tends to be on a large scale with high numbers of casualties. Because of this, regulations against alcohol and drugs have always tended to be tight, especially with airlines.

Regulations do differ between airlines but most insist upon pilots and crew abstaining from alcohol for between 8 and 24 hours prior to flying.

The whole matter was particularly highlighted in the USA in 1990 by the conviction of three pilots of Northwest Airlines for flying a jet liner with 91 passengers on board whilst intoxicated. In the USA, it is an offence to fly an aeroplane within eight hours of drinking or with a blood alcohol level exceeding 40 mg. As a result of strict Federal Aviation Authority controls on all airline employees and potential employees, failure rates on random alcohol and drug tests are very low, greatly increasing the safety factor for all travellers[16].

The potential problems in aviation that led to legislation in many countries were highlighted by a survey carried out some years ago in the USA, in which it was established that over a four-year period one-third of 900 private pilots killed in air crashes had alcohol in their blood[17]. Another report covering 158 accidents showed that 56 pilots gave positive results when tested for blood alcohol[18]. In addition to this, it was shown that 10% of fatal aviation accidents in the USA between 1975 and 1981 involved alcohol[19] and led to nearly 1000 people being killed or injured. However, these were not scheduled passenger services.

Tests which have been carried out using experienced pilots on special instrument trainers[20] have shown clearly that the ability to pilot an aircraft can be impaired by blood alcohol levels as low as 20 mg and studies on groups of professional and non-professional pilots showed that, even with blood alcohol levels as low as 40 mg, they carried out manoeuvres which were hazardous, and at levels of 120 mg their flying was so appalling that the non-drinking co-pilot had to take over the controls[21]. Similarly, tests on flight simulators[22] have shown that *serious* errors are made even at blood alcohol levels as low as 25 mg.

In addition to this, it should be pointed out that at altitude the physiological effect of alcohol is enhanced due to the decreased amount of oxygen available, so there is a greater impairment of a pilot's abilities and a corresponding increase in the likelihood of making an error of judgement.

However, it is not just pilots who need to avoid alcohol and drugs. Passenger safety is equally dependent upon the skills and care of alert, sober maintenance workers and flight controllers. Certainly, there is every reason for authorities to continue to exercise very strict controls in all aspects of aviation.

Many countries now operate blanket laws, such as those established in the Transport and Works Act 1992 in Great Britain, which make it an offence for any transport worker in a safety sensitive post to arrive at work having taken alcohol or drugs. There has certainly been a considerable tightening up in this area since it was shown that levels of drinking by airline pilots increased substantially after years of flying jet aircraft[23]. Fortunately, that is very much a thing of the past with the regular tests and medical checks which are now carried out. Certainly, passengers on the major civil aviation airlines can rest assured that, with regular health surveys and a general watchful approach, they are highly unlikely to be piloted by anyone under the influence of alcohol. However, a few more breath testing machines at airports throughout the world would still not be amiss.

Alcohol and rail transport

For many years the preoccupation of governments and safety authorities with the drinking driver actually meant that the possible involvement of alcohol and drugs with other transport accidents was substantially ignored. This often led to anomalies in which bus and coach drivers would be covered by drink-drive regulations and have to submit to breath and blood tests after being involved in accidents, whilst train drivers were not. In some instances, the introduction of controls and legislation has not always been supported by transport trade unions, in the misguided belief that such controls were contrary to the interests of their members, despite the fact that the drinking or drugged train driver is a serious danger to other rail workers[24].

In the USA, attention was drawn to the drinking practices of railway workers by a report in 1979[25]. Nearly a quarter of a million railway workers were surveyed. Of these, 12% admitted to having drunk alcohol whilst on duty at least three times during the previous year and, of even greater importance, was the fact that 20% admitted to having been drunk on duty at least once during the year.

The consequences of alcohol related railway accidents are horrific. Sweedler[19] reported that 19 railway accidents in which alcohol and/or drugs were shown to have been involved cost 27 lives, led to 15 other people being injured and produced $26 million in property damage. Reported railway accidents in the USA involved workers with blood alcohol levels of 220 mg (a driver), 340 mg (another driver) and 110 mg (a brakeman). It was as a result of these studies and a rail accident involving a driver with a blood alcohol level of 210 mg that the Omnibus Transportation Employee Testing Act was introduced in 1991 and led to an enormous expansion in alcohol and drug testing in the transport industry as a whole in the USA. This now covers nearly eight million employees[16] and has brought about an improvement such that positive results are now occurring in fewer than 1% of all tests.

Fortunately, serious rail accidents arising from drinking are very rare but, however uncommon rail deaths may be, it should not be forgotten that a drunken train driver caused the death of six people at Eltham, England in 1972 by travelling at 65 mph around a 20 mph controlled curve. It should also be borne in mind that, until recently, checks on blood alcohol levels of pilots, train drivers, boatmen and other workers were only compulsory if they had died in an accident and the examination was carried out as part of an autopsy. At one time in Great Britain it was quite common to read of guards and signalmen being drunk on duty and a London newspaper in 1982 reported[26] that train crews and station staff were seen openly flaunting rules which banned London Regional Transport staff from drinking at work. The resulting enquiry following this report undoubtedly led to some tightening up at the time but many people continued totally to ignore the fact that their lives and those of other people were put at risk by them turning a blind eye to their drinking colleagues.

Even after this, cases of drunken railway workers continued to occur. For instance, in 1983 a drunken signalman[27] in Tiverton, Devon fell asleep in his signal box so that contact was lost with five trains over a 17 mile stretch of railway. Fortunately, on this particular occasion no damage or injury was suffered by anybody, thanks to the careful actions of other railway workers; but the stupidity of one man placed an enormously increased and unnecessary responsibility on many others to avoid accidents.

As with the USA, it was the result of a train accident that actually brought the matter of testing train drivers in Great Britain to a head. In January 1991, the driver of a train that hit the buffers at Cannon Street Station, London was allowed to leave the scene of the accident and was not tested for anything until 48 hours later. After that lengthy delay it was totally irrelevant that the driver was found to have metabolites of cannabis in his urine[28]. However, the publicity of this case fortunately led to very rapid parliamentary action.

The introduction of the Transport and Works Act 1992 occurred as a direct result of pressures arising from this type of public transport accident. In the case of the London underground, it meant that workers were required to abstain from drinking alcohol for 8 hours before arriving at work and to drink no more than four pints of beer during the previous 16 hours. Random testing for alcohol and drugs was introduced for most underground workers[29].

Similar restrictions and controls are now being extended to other public transport sectors but Great Britain has yet to follow the example of the USA in imposing a 40 mg blood alcohol limit for all drivers in the mass transportation industry.

The responsibility of workers

Any employee working with machinery, driving tractors or fork-lift trucks or carrying out precision operations should not drink prior to or during working hours. Throughout the European Union and North America there is increasing concern about the working environment, not least in seeking to reduce working hazards. It is now firmly accepted that one worker can create dangers for another due to carelessness and negligence. In Britain, all workers became responsible for the safety of their colleagues[30] as a result of the Health and Safety at Work Act 1974. One of the consequences of this Act of Parliament has been that it is possible for an injured person to take legal action if an industrial injury occurs as a result of the action or inaction of a drunken work-mate.

This may well lead to some interesting court cases in the future as, in various countries, people have been prosecuted for being drunk in charge of such odd vehicles as tanks, snow ploughs, a motorised vacuum cleaner, electric milk floats and tractors. So it is not only the ordinary motorist who is in danger, but anyone using mobile equipment such as cranes, earthmovers, diggers and roadsweepers.

Alcohol-related accidents have occurred in the most unexpected circumstances. For instance, the increased popularity of snowmobiling in Canada led to 586 people dying in crashes between 1987 and 1993. Of the 480 drivers killed, 76% had been drinking and, of those with alcohol in their bodies, eight out of every ten had blood alcohol levels in excess of 80 mg.

In countries in which motor vehicles are still uncommon, drink-driving is often associated with other forms of transport. For instance, in Croatia it was found[31] that more than 60% of tractor drivers involved in accidents had been drinking and more than half of the accidents had occurred whilst working in the fields.

With the increased emphasis against alcohol in the workplace, it is clear that there is a corresponding danger that people will tend to drink more heavily when they are relaxing or taking part in leisure pursuits. Nevertheless, as has already been pointed out, alcohol and precision activities and/or dangerous machinery do not mix.

Alcohol in aquatic and marine environments

Nowhere should the warning against alcohol and its potential dangers be emphasised more strongly than in aquatic and marine environments. Whilst this is still an area which has not been fully investigated, studies from France, Finland and the USA again show a disproportionate involvement of alcohol in deaths during boating, swimming and climbing. Concern has been particularly expressed about the dangers inherent in going swimming after even moderate drinking of alcohol. This is easily done in a careless moment, especially when people are enjoying themselves while relaxing on holiday and it can have tragic results due to swimmers choking, misjudging diving or swimming too far out to sea.

One of the few organisations which has addressed itself to the problem of alcohol and swimming is the Royal Life Saving Society of Canada[32] which has clearly spelt out the combined dangers of drinking alcohol prior to swimming and of taking alcohol into the aquatic environment, be it around a swimming pool or on to a beach. Unambiguous statistics which identify the number of drowned swimmers having alcohol in their bodies, as distinct from drowned seamen and boaters who have been drinking, are difficult to obtain, but one thing that does come out quite clearly is the very large proportion of people who have elevated levels of alcohol in their bodies. For instance, one study[33] has shown that alcohol played a part in 50% of the drownings of Norwegian seamen, whilst another[34], in Australia, showed that 11 out of 18 recovered bodies of people who had fallen off jetties or boats had blood alcohol levels exceeding 150 mg. Such a high involvement of alcohol appears to be both occupation (seamen) and age related. The Royal Life Saving Society in Great Britain found[35] that alcohol was a relevant factor in 38% of drownings in the 25-29 age group. This was double the percentage for alcohol involvement in all drownings in 1983. It is important in this context to point out that the drinker is in danger of drowning irrespective of his or her swimming ability. An investigation in the USA showed that, of 45 drownings which were investigated[36], 40% had blood alcohol levels exceeding 100 mg and nearly four-fifths of these were considered to be good swimmers.

That wider involvement of alcohol in aquatic accidents in general tends to be under-reported has been clearly demonstrated in studies by the National Transportation Safety Board in the USA[19]. In 1982, there were 1178 fatalities from boating in that country. 90% of these were due to drowning and it has been shown that alcohol might have been involved in more than two-thirds of them. Individual states in the USA which have made special studies of alcohol involvement have shown that between 40% and 80% of water craft deaths involve alcohol, with blood alcohol levels often above 100 mg.

These figures have been supported by a ten-year study of boating deaths in Finland[37] where there is a legal blood alcohol limit of 150 mg on water. It was found that, of the death rate of about 100 per annum in boating incidents, nearly two-thirds of the fatalities were under the influence of alcohol and many died due to their unwillingness to wear the mandatory life-jacket. The study also showed that the likelihood of having an accident increased with the blood alcohol level and a curve of the type shown in Figure 8 (page 53) applied. In this case, the accident potential was shown to increase eight-fold by the 50 mg level.

It is quite clear that further, more detailed studies into alcohol and aquatic deaths are justified with special safety campaigns directed to the leisure and vacation drinker. All too often what should be a period of rest and relaxation can become a time of tragedy. Despite this, there has been a strong outcry against the suggestion in Great Britain that there should be a legal blood alcohol level for boaters.

It should not be forgotten that, even if death by drowning does not occur, the control (or lack of control) of boats and ships by those who have been drinking adds to the hazards at sea for others[38]. As long ago as 1969, a Committee of Inquiry set up by the British Board of Trade found that there was strong evidence that the safety of fishing vessels was being put at risk by the drinking of the crews of trawlers[39], but various prosecutions over the years do not appear to have had a very great effect, as the following events have shown:

(a) In 1980, the captain of an emergency stand-by boat for an oil-rig had his certificate suspended for ten years after it was found that he and three of his four crew were drunk when his ship went aground on a sandbank[40].

(b) Following a daytime collision between the *Leswood* and the *Astra*, legal action was taken in Edinburgh, Scotland against some of the crew of the *Leswood* after it was found that cans of beer had been distributed at regular intervals to the crew and the person in charge of the watch at the time of the collision had also been drinking whisky.

(c) When the trawler *Wyre Victory* struck the rocks of the Hebrides in 1976, it was because the steersman was drunk from having had 12 cans of beer and half a bottle of whisky. His state was such that he was incapable of responding to the situation despite the fact that a warning lighthouse beam was shining regularly into the wheelhouse.

However, there are few accidents that can rival that of the *Exxon Valdez* disaster in 1989 that caused such enormous environmental damage in Alaska due to spilling 10.8 million gallons of oil. Following the conviction of the captain, who had a long history of heavy drinking, there were immediate calls for tighter maritime regulations to deal with alcohol and drug abuse[41].

Despite such tragedies, there are still cases of seamen running their ships aground or trying to steer their vessels through dangerous shipping lanes when highly intoxicated[42].

There really is no end to these stories or the tales of horror, appalling deaths, terrible injuries and family suffering that arise as a direct consequence of inconsiderate drinking. If drinkers only put their own lives at risk that would be bad enough but at least that is their right. It is the fact that, both directly and indirectly, they endanger the lives of many others as well as involving society in an enormous financial cost that makes their actions selfish, inconsiderate, anti-social and reprehensible. You do not need to be rolling drunk to be a danger to other people.

Now that the dangers of alcohol on the roads, in the home, at work and at play have been recognised, there is a need for greater education of the public to these dangers. A greater awareness by all drinkers coupled with an increased use of breath and blood tests in the working environment would go a long way to creating a more responsible attitude to drinking.

The message must be, take extra-special care at all times if you have been drinking and if in doubt – don't.

Chapter 10

ALCOHOL, EDUCATION AND THE FUTURE

"Licence they mean when they cry Liberty,
For who loves that, must first be wise and good."
John Milton

In the area of alcohol, drugs and accidents an uncomfortable alliance between science, medicine and the law is found to exist. The medical problems concerning the use and abuse of alcohol and other drugs are well established and the scientific procedures for the measurement of levels in blood, urine and other body fluids are also well established. However, these do not always lead to simply written laws or even to straightforward specific answers to the questions that might be asked in court. It is often forgotten that the forensic medical examiner, chemist and pharmacist called as expert witnesses are not there to ensure either a conviction or an acquittal. Their role is to try and present what may frequently be complicated scientific data in a manner that will enable it to be readily understood. This is done without bias or prejudice, irrespective of whether they have been called as witnesses by the defence or the prosecution.

That the services of such experts are still frequently needed is evidence of the difficulty of writing unambiguous laws in relation to matters such as these. Science and law are frequently uneasy bedfellows. All countries that have legislated on drinking and driving have found that, irrespective of the care that may have been devoted to the drafting of the law, accused drivers and their lawyers will do their best to find a loophole in that law in order to save the driving licence or avoid a heavy fine or a prison sentence. Drink-drive legislation, requiring the use of scientific procedures, inevitably gives rise to a high proportion of ingenious defences and claims.

159

There can be no simple or short answer to the problems associated with drinking, drugs and driving. It is obvious that only sustained efforts over a long period of time will achieve and maintain permanent success in this battle to reduce the accident figures. There is no doubt that the continual carnage on the roads attributable to the drinking and/or drugged driver well justifies tougher laws and stronger enforcement. However, it is generally accepted that laws and regulations have little likelihood of success in democratic countries unless they have the respect and support of the majority of citizens. Fortunately, during the past ten years there has been a swing away from the "there but for the grace of God go I" attitude to the drinking driver. High profile road safety campaigns and civic bodies have played a major role in educating the public and increasing the awareness of the true magnitude of the problem of the intoxicated driver.

But there are still weaknesses in this. The indications are that a very high proportion of banned drivers still continue to drive after they have been convicted and ordered to stay off the road[1], so they remain a danger to other road users, especially as they are likely to be uninsured. The public often do not know if their friend, relation or neighbour has been convicted of this type of offence because the conviction is rarely listed in the local newspaper, unless there has been some special factor to excite the local or national press. Greater media publicity with a weekly list of banned motorists would increase the stigma against the drinking driver and help ensure that those who have had their licences revoked actually stay off the roads.

Political decisions and road safety

It appears from accident figures that the introduction of modern instruments, lower blood alcohol limits, severer penalties and more powerful road safety campaigns have managed to reduce casualty figures substantially in many countries. However, it is not possible to relax the vigilance in any way. There are always new and younger motorists joining those already on the road; there are those drivers who drink more heavily after they have been banned and continue to do so when they receive their licences back again; there are always those who do not care and believe that the laws should be ignored; and there are those who cannot believe that a small amount of alcohol plus their officially prescribed drugs taken together can make them a danger. It is because of these that reassessments and new approaches are necessary at all times to maintain general public awareness and responsibility in a realm of human activity that has led to so much tragedy over the years.

Unfortunately, many of the decisions that have to be taken in this field are both strongly political and financial. The motoring sector in any country is very powerful in terms of the votes that can be wielded and political parties are not always prepared to take steps that could antagonise this section of the population – particularly if there is any possibility of the politicians having to face re-election shortly after legislating tighter controls. Coupled to this is the reluctance of some governments to take steps that might cause too drastic a drop in the revenues arising from sales of alcoholic drinks. For these reasons, road safety proposals involving restrictions on the individual, which are interpreted as being limitations on personal rights and freedoms, are deferred or watered down.

Nor does it come as any surprise to learn that control of the drunken driver has tended to move very slowly in countries which are major wine producers with powerful agricultural lobbies. Fortunately, even the alcohol producing industries now appreciate that their public image and potential markets do not benefit from those people who drink to excess and cause mayhem when under the influence of alcohol.

High risk offenders

Moves to deal with the problems of the high risk offender do indicate that a considerable change has taken place in the public attitude towards the heavy drinker. There is no exact medical meaning of the term 'alcoholism' but it is used extensively to apply to people who have serious alcohol-related problems and are alcohol-dependent. There is certainly a greater awareness that alcohol dependency is an illness which requires proper medical treatment and counselling[2] and it is well recognised that harsher and harsher penalties do not necessarily lead to any change or improvement in the drinker's approach. The driver who regularly attains blood alcohol levels well over 100 mg is a person likely to have a drinking problem and will possibly be approaching alcoholism. For such people, the approach must be one of information, education and rehabilitation, while at the same time ensuring that they are not allowed the freedom of the road. In this respect, the use of 200 mg for the 'high-risk', first time offender, accepted by the British Government, is far too high. Most other countries that have looked at this have considered that the danger point justifying special attention is 150 mg (65 μg in breath). It is quite obvious that far more concern must be given to improved treatment for problem drinkers in all walks of life as various studies show that they are involved in a disproportionate number of accidents and misdemeanours[3].

Few people are aware that, internationally, the high-risk offender and recidivist drink-driver is receiving special legislative and medical attention. The automatic regranting of driving licences now does not always apply. Drivers who have been convicted twice for drink-drive offences are likely to find themselves having to undergo medical tests to show they do not have a drink problem and re-take their driving tests. Even then, conditions may be imposed on their driving, in some cases requiring the use of inter-lock safety devices necessitating a breath sample before their car can be driven[4]. Greater efforts are being made to keep the high-risk offender and repeat offender off the road in order to increase safety for everyone.

Young drinkers

In many ways, by the time the problem has become one of adult alcoholism it is almost too late, as the progression to heavy drinking is frequently a long one starting at a fairly early age. The very high accident rate amongst teenage motorcyclists, coupled with the early age at which many children first drink alcohol[5], shows very strongly that the campaign of education on the dangers of drink and drugs must start in the homes and schools in order to encourage a healthy and responsible attitude to alcohol before the habit is acquired. There is clear evidence that alcohol and drug abuse is occurring with very young teenagers[6] and this will inevitably be reflected in accident figures and problem drinkers in the years ahead.

It is extremely short-sighted to direct the road safety advertising campaigns to those who have already obtained driving licences and attained the age at which they can purchase alcoholic drinks. Alcohol and drug awareness programmes need to be directed at school children at quite a young age in order to develop a responsible attitude.

Too many parents and schools are seeking to ignore the very real deterioration that is occurring around them. Yet it is possible to engender a more reasoned and balanced approach to alcohol at a very early age by example, guidance and instruction[7]. Obviously, a much greater effort in this area is essential. Parents must accept responsibility for guiding their children away from the dangers of heavy drinking by demonstrating that they themselves do not drink to excess or drive after having been drinking. Children should be able to take pride in saying "My Dad and Mum don't drink and drive!".

Growth of public opinion

Fortunately, there has been a groundswell of public opinion building up against the drinking driver. Mothers Against Drunk Drivers now has chapters (branches) in nearly all American states as well as in other countries, and is receiving increasing support from the general public, especially those who have lost friends and relations in drink-drive accidents. It is no longer considered to be clever to drive with alcohol in your body. Certainly, the only way to bring the message home to many people is to make sure it is firm, clear and hard-hitting. Soft-sell campaigns such as the 'Stay Low' pre-Christmas 1984 approach in Great Britain appear to have little effect.

That particular campaign aimed at persuading the young

driver to act more responsibly with respect to drink was a dismal failure – simply because 'stay low' meant different things to different people. For some drivers, limiting themselves to five or six pints of beer was 'staying low' because they normally drank nine or ten pints at a time. The campaign was, in fact, an encouragement to drink and the number of motorists giving positive breath tests increased over Christmas 1984 compared with the previous year. The effective campaigns appear to be those which clearly draw attention to the dangers and horrors of alcohol-related accidents.

It is, of course, not just in the home and on the roads where concern about alcohol exists. The industrial environment is now receiving increasing attention and, in future, even greater restrictions on alcohol in factories and greater control of employees who have been drinking will become essential. Studies around the world have clearly shown that a major proportion of industrial accidents occur due to drinking and increased dependence on the use of computers and precision equipment means that employees cannot afford to have their senses and responses dulled by a liquid lunch. There is no doubt that keyboard errors increase substantially at very low blood alcohol levels. It has been known[8] for many years that the much loved combination of gin and tonic at lunchtime gives rise to hypoglycaemia, a reduction in the blood sugar level, and that this may actually be aggravated by eating sandwiches at the same time. The hypoglycaemia produced may be the cause of the afternoon fatigue that is so common around 3.00 p.m. and that is associated with working accidents.

Company managers and trade union leaders are becoming increasingly concerned about the dangers that can be created for their members due to heavy drinkers working with machinery, heavy loads and driving vehicles at work. Alcohol abuse is costing industry millions of pounds every year due to illness, absenteeism, accidents and damage. It is from this area that greater pressures are growing for checks on blood alcohol levels of workers involved in accidents and for supervisors to require breath tests for people who may come on duty after drinking. Industrial safety is everybody's concern and is just as important to the machine-shop worker as to the company salesman driving his car[9].

Drink and drugs

This particular chapter would not be complete without mention of the realm of the combination of alcohol and drugs. It is a fact that other drugs are frequently found in the blood of a proportion of people killed in road accidents. The driving laws in most countries are aimed at both alcohol and drug takers, although the former are more readily detected. What is particularly bad is the number of people who still drink alcohol when taking normal prescribed drugs – despite the fact that some combinations can be lethal[10].

Many prescribed drugs are themselves sedative in character, including many analgesics, barbiturates, antihistamines and benzodiazepines. In combination with even small quantities of alcohol, there can frequently be a potentiating effect by which the level of sedation is greatly increased. Under these circumstances, any driving ability, concentration or response time is greatly impaired. The same problem exists with people taking illegal drugs such as heroin, morphine and cannabis. In many instances, the results of alcohol/drugs combinations can be variable and unpredictable, but often highly dangerous, as with hallucinogenic drugs like LSD or the stimulants such as amphetamine and ecstasy. Alcohol can be dangerous enough by itself but in combination with drugs it can be, and often is, lethal[11].

There is a great need for medical practitioners to advise their patients better about any dangers associated with the drugs they prescribe. At the same time, manufacturers and pharmacies should be required, when appropriate, to label drug containers with a clear warning against drinking alcohol or driving whilst under the influence of the drug.

Studies are now under way to develop rapid roadside screening tests that can be used for detecting drugs in a driver's body. Breath is obviously unsuitable for this purpose as the drugs are not volatile enough to be exhaled in most cases. It is, however, possible that various chemical tests on saliva can be used to give suitable colour reactions in the presence of the most common drugs and the day (or night) of the roadside drug test may not be far away. Already, chemical kits are available for police and customs officers to be able to check for drugs in the solid state by simple chemical spot tests and these are used to study suspect powders and liquids at airports and docks. Roadside tests in Germany[12] have already shown that saliva is of immense value in testing for drugs. Procedures are now available for carrying out rapid roadside analyses for drugs in urine[13], using specially built mini-laboratories in trailers. Very soon, mobile facilities will enable the police to stop motorists and carry out on-the-spot qualitative, evidential tests for alcohol and drugs, rather than just screening tests.

Post-mortems on road accident victims do include checks for the presence of common drugs and it is from these investigations that the figures for drug involvement are obtained. However, it cannot be denied that alcohol is by far the most common drug to be found.

Self-testing devices

Many people who do drink and also drive cars or motorcycles are anxious to do their best to keep within the law. For this reason there has been an increasing demand for self-testing devices. This type of pressure originally led to the British Government agreeing to permit the sale of roadside screening devices to the public. However, there is no encouragement from either motoring associations or the police for self-testing in Great Britain.

Self-testing in bars and clubs is much more common in Australia, Canada and the USA, where wall-mounted testing units in bars and restaurants are quite common. Similarly, self-testing has been common in France since the big police clampdown on drink-drivers in 1978 when the manufacturers of the tube-and-bag device could not keep up with demand.

The most extensive studies on self-testing have been carried out in Australia, where there are at least half-a-dozen instrument manufacturers. It has been clearly demonstrated[14] that modern instruments are accurate and reliable so long as they are regularly serviced and correctly used[15].

Despite public demand, the Blennerhasset Committee in Britain came out against self-testing on the basis that requests for guidance on how much can be drunk to stay below the legal limit "suggest a widespread and dangerous assumption that it is safe to drink up to the level". In fact, nobody has produced any evidence to suggest that people use such devices to drink to the limit, but rather that they use them to monitor that they have not reached the limit. The opposition to self-testing depends upon totally subjective statements unsubstantiated by experimental data. If, however, the Blennerhassett Committee was correct in its view, then two things need to be done. First, self-testing and the sale of self-testing devices should be banned and the evidence to justify this action should be published for all to read. Secondly, the statement quoted above is a clear acceptance that the 80 mg level is too high and is misleading people into drinking too heavily, so should be lowered to 50 mg.

On the assumption that no government has the political courage to take these actions, then self-testing will continue and increase. It is, therefore, essential that steps be taken to establish some form of standard by which such equipment can be assessed and to require that routine maintenance be properly carried out. If approached in the right manner, self-testing may also play its part in helping to reduce the number of road casualties.

No future for the drinking driver

The past few years have seen a move away from the short-term, seasonally based drink-drive campaigns usually directed at the public during Christmas, the New Year or Thanksgiving. Studies showed that the actual number of alcohol-related road deaths during these periods were frequently well below normal daily averages. This has meant a change of policy, with campaigns targeted towards high risk groups, such as younger drivers, or periods of long, hot weather conditions when drinking is likely to become greater. Greater emphasis is being placed on making the drinking driver feel self-conscious and guilty for putting other people at risk. Needless to say, such road safety campaigns do not receive the endorsement of everyone but they have been impressive and highly memorable.

Future anti-drink-driving campaigns need to be very broadly directed as a whole range of areas for improvements still remain. There is no doubt that alcohol-related deaths on the road, in the home and at work can still be greatly reduced. The following are actions that can, for the greater part, be easily carried out:

1. Greater guidance for young children and teenagers about the dangers of alcohol and drugs.

2. Advice for everyone against giving alcoholic drinks to drivers or going in a car with a driver who has been drinking.

3. Lower legal drink-drive limits, with an international objective of a maximum of 50 mg.

4. Clear, unambiguous labelling of the percentage alcohol content of *all* alcoholic drinks at *all* times, with beers and lagers graded and colour-coded into non, low, weak, medium, strong and very strong grades.

5. 'Don't drink and drive' notices clearly displayed in all public houses, bars, clubs and restaurants.

6. Breath tests for *all* road-users involved in road accidents.

7. Improved treatment for problem drinkers.

8. Much clearer advice for patients from GPs and pharmacists against the danger of combining their prescribed drugs with alcohol.

Any campaign against drinking drivers should be at least as strong as that against smoking and could well lead eventually to a ban on the advertising of alcohol, as suggested by the British Medical Association and other public bodies.

The evils and tragedies associated with excess drinking cannot be considered as just a thing of the past. It has been calculated that, in the USA, 50% of the population will be involved in an accident with a drunk driver at some time during their lifetime and the chances of being killed by a drunk driver are nearly 15 times greater than being shot.

The orgies of ancient Rome and the commentaries of Hogarth have been replaced by the lager lout at sporting events, the secret drinker and the drunken road-user. History has shown that prohibition is not an answer to this problem. Success will only come by well designed laws, and firm and fair law enforcement coupled with a better informed public and greater social stigma against those who endanger the lives of other people. The problem still remains one of getting people to appreciate their physical limitations when drinking alcohol and educating them into accepting their social responsibilities within society. This should start with 'None for the Road'.

APPENDIX

Ethanol and Its Chemical Reactions

Ethanol, the active constituent of alcoholic beverages, is the second member of a series of closely related chemical compounds known collectively as the 'alcohols'. Also included in this group are methanol, propanol and butanol, along with many others. The alcohols consist of a combination of carbon, hydrogen and oxygen atoms, expressed by chemists in a shorthand form as:

CH_3OH	methanol
CH_3CH_2OH	ethanol
$CH_3CH_2CH_2OH$	propanol
$CH_3CH_2CH_2CH_2OH$	butanol

Ethanol is the most well known 'alcohol' because it is the one readily prepared by fermentation processes. Large quantities of all the common alcohols are manufactured by industrial processes and are used widely as solvents and in the manufacture of other chemicals.

Methods available for the chemical analysis of ethanol in blood, urine and breath samples can be classified into two groups. The first of these are qualitative tests – so called because they are only used to show the existence of ethanol but not necessarily the amount present. The second group are the quantitative tests employed to determine the amount of ethanol present, within an established level of accuracy. It will be appreciated that, whilst a quantitative test may also be a qualitative test, the converse is not necessarily true.

The tube and bag breath test device which has been used extensively in Great Britain and other European countries is basically a rough quantitative measure developed from a qualitative test. Because of this, its accuracy is rather limited and it is only suitable as a screening test in those instances in which people are either near or over the legal limit. Of

171

necessity, a more precise analysis is required after a positive response to the screening test has been obtained and this is the reason for taking a blood or urine sample for analysis or an evidential breath test using more sophisticated instruments.

The chemical tests employed for checking the presence and quantity of ethanol are based upon the reactions it will undergo when treated with chemical reagents known as oxidising agents. These are chemicals which are able to supply oxygen to a system to bring about a chemical change on other substances; in this case on the ethanol. In the chemical reactions mentioned throughout this book, attack by oxidising agents leads to a progressive breakdown of the structure of ethanol. Oxidation takes place in three distinct steps depending upon the amount of oxygen supplied to the reacting systems.

In the first step, a limited amount of available oxygen leads to the formation of acetaldehyde (ethanal). In chemical terms this is represented by the following equation:

$$CH_3CH_2OH \xrightarrow{[O]} CH_3CHO + H_2O \quad (1)$$

ethanol · · · · · · · · · · · · · acetaldehyde · · · water

With a larger amount of available oxygen the oxidation proceeds further, producing acetic acid (ethanoic acid), represented by a second chemical equation:

$$CH_3CHO \xrightarrow{[O]} CH_3COOH \quad (2)$$

acetaldehyde · · · · · · · · · · · · · acetic acid

Under more severe reaction conditions, the acetic acid is oxidised to its maximum extent to form carbon dioxide and water, as represented in the third equation:

$$CH_3COOH \xrightarrow{[O]} 2\ CO_2 + 2\ H_2O \quad (3)$$

acetic acid · · · · · · · · · · · carbon dioxide · · water

Many chemicals are capable of supplying the oxygen required for these reactions to occur but, in practice, only a few well-established systems are employed. In the instruments involving wet chemical processes for breath alcohol testing, the most common reagent is a mixture of potassium dichromate and sulphuric acid. An intense yellow-orange solution is produced when the two substances are mixed together. If a reactive substance such as ethanol is added to the solution, a colour change from yellow-orange to blue-green takes place. The new coloration is due to the formation of chromium sulphate in the reaction mixture. This is the cause of the green colour that arises when breath containing alcohol is blown through the crystals in the tube and bag roadside screening device. The oxygen needed for the oxidation of the alcohol is produced according to the chemical equation:

$$2\,K_2Cr_2O_7 + 8\,H_2SO_4 \rightarrow 2\,Cr_2(SO_4)_3 + 2\,K_2SO_4 + 8\,H_2O + 6[O]$$

| potassium dichromate | sulphuric acid | chromium sulphate | potassium sulphate | water | oxygen |

The oxygen from this reaction is responsible for converting the ethanol to acetaldehyde and ultimately to acetic acid according to equations (1) and (2) as already described. The further conversion to carbon dioxide and water (equation 3) only occurs if potassium dichromate/sulphuric acid solution is heated with the ethanol.

The intensity of the green colour that is formed in this system is a measure of the amount of alcohol that is present and the laboratory application of the method is dependent upon using carefully measured concentrations of specially purified chemicals in order that any margin of error is kept to a minimum in the quantitative determinations. The first quantitative measure of ethanol by this system was carried out as long ago as 1865 and the procedure has been used and improved extensively during the past 100 years. As a result of this work, an experienced analyst can determine the amount of alcohol in a sample of blood or urine within an accuracy of ±5%. Most of the colour change reactions tend to be used more for screening purposes than for evidential quantitative testing.

It will be obvious that the accuracy of colour reactions depends upon many factors, including the absence of other compounds likely to be oxidised by the reagents. The quantitative value of these reactions only exists if the analyst first removes any substance likely to interfere with the test. This can usually be achieved with a laboratory procedure but is not likely to be entirely possible in roadside tests.

In the enzymatic oxidation method used for rapid quantitative alcohol analysis, especially in hospitals, a yeast enzyme, alcohol dehydrogenase (ADH), is used in conjunction with a coenzyme, nicotinamide adenine dinucleotide (NAD^+). ADH is the same enzyme as the one responsible for breaking down alcohol in the human liver. The biochemical oxidation process leads to the formation of acetaldehyde and the quantity of alcohol is determined from the formation of the reduced form of NAD^+ which can be measured spectrometrically at 340 nm. In some variations on this reaction, the NADH is used to produce highly coloured formazan derivatives which can be used to produce enhanced sensitivity for the method. The equation for the main reaction is usually represented as:

$$CH_3CH_2OH + NAD^+ \xrightarrow{\text{ADH}} CH_3CHO + NADH + H^+$$

Many public analysts have discontinued using the above wet chemical methods for accurate determination of the ethanol in blood and urine samples submitted to them. Instead, they resort to the technique of gas chromatography, described in detail in Chapter 7, in which all volatile substances present in the samples can be separated from each other and individually measured. Chemical colour reactions are still employed in several ways in portable forms of apparatus used for kerbside tests of breath alcohol throughout the world. For these purposes, the potassium dichromate system is still popular but now tends to be kept as a stand-by test having given way to the portable electronic screening instruments, based upon semi-conductors and fuel cells.

REFERENCES

In the following lists a number of publications, in addition to standard scientific journals and newspapers, are referred to several times. In these instances, the title of the volume is presented in an abbreviated form, as shown below:

Blennerhassett – *Report of the Departmental Committee on Drinking and Driving*, F Blennerhassett (Chairman), HMSO, London, 16 February (1976).

Chem. Test Intoxic. – *Chemical Tests for Intoxication*, H A Heise (ed.), American Medical Association, Chicago, (1959).

Methods Foren. Sci. – *Methods of Forensic Science*, A S Curry (ed.), Vol 4, Interscience, London and New York, (1965).

Proceedings of International Conferences on Alcohol, Drugs and Traffic Safety

Proc. 3rd Int. Conf. (1962) – J D J Havard (ed.), British Medical Association, London, (1963).

Proc. 4th Int. Conf. (1965) – R Harger (ed.), Indiana University, Bloomington, (1966).

Proc. 6th Int. Conf. (1974) – S Israelstam & S Lambert (eds.), Addiction Research Foundation, Toronto, (1975).

Proc. 8th Int. Conf. (1980) – L Goldberg (ed.), Almquist and Wiksell International, Stockholm, (1981).

Proc. 9th Int. Conf. (1983) – S Kaye (ed.), US Department of Transport, (1985).

Proc. 10th Int. Conf. (1986) – P C Noordzij & R Roszbach (eds.), Excerpta Medica, Amsterdam, (1987).

Proc. 11th Int. Conf. (1989) – M W B Perrine (ed.), National Safety Council, Chicago, (1990).

Proc. 12th Int. Conf. (1992) – H D Utzelmann, G Berghaus & G Kroj (eds.), Verlag TUV Rheinland, Cologne, (1993).

Proc. 13th Int. Conf. (1995) – C N Kloeden & A J McLean (eds.), The University of Adelaide, (1995).

Introduction

1. T Shumel, 'Traffic Safety in Developing Countries: a Troubling Prognosis', *J. Prevention Routier Internationale*, (1987), [1], 50.

2. R C Denney, *The Truth About Breath Tests*, Nelson, London, (1970), 69.

Chapter 1 – Alcohol, Its Origin, Use and Abuse

1. C J S Thompson, *The Lure and Romance of Alchemy*, Bell Publishing Company, New York, (1990), 135.

2. M B Kreig, *Green Medicine*, G C Harrap & Co. Ltd., London, (1965), 152.

3. A Bryant, *Samuel Pepys – The Man in the Making*, Cambridge University Press, (1933), 41.

4. T Babor, 'Alcohol – Customs and Rituals', Vol 2 in the *Encyclopaedia of Psychoactive Drugs*, S H Snyder & M H Lader (eds.), Burk Publishing Co. Ltd., London, (1988), 20.

5. *Michael Jackson's Pocket Beer Book*, Mitchell Beazley Ltd., London, (1981), 7.

6. *Holy Bible*, Genesis 9 v 21.

7. *Holy Bible*, Genesis 19 v 32–35.

8. F Bergel and D R A Davies, *All About Drugs*, T Nelson & Sons Ltd., (1970), 23.

9. A Barr, *Wine Snobbery*, Faber & Faber Ltd., London, (1988), 177.

10. H Johnson, *The World Atlas of Wine*, 4th edn., Mitchell Beazley Ltd., London, (1994), 298.

11. *Alcohol Concern*, (1994), 9, [1], 5.

12. *Holy Bible*, Proverbs 20 v 1.

13. J Howell, 'Familiar Letter to the Lord Cliffe, 1634' in *The Pageant of English Prose*, R M Leonard (ed.), Oxford University Press, (1912), 331–333.

14. W Shakespeare, *King Henry IV, Part II*, Act 4, Scene III.

15. W Shakespeare, *Macbeth*, Act 2, Scene III.

16. J O'Connor, *The Young Drinkers*, Tavistock Publications, London, (1978), 42.

17. A Cooke, *Alistair Cooke's America*, British Broadcasting Corporation, London, (1973), 324.

18. S E Morison, *The Oxford History of the American People*, Oxford University Press, New York, (1965), 899.

19. A Barr, *Wine Snobbery*, Faber & Faber Ltd., London, (1988), pp. ix and 152.

20. Spirits (Strengths Ascertainment) Act 1818, HMSO, London.

21. Customs and Excise Act 1952, section 172, HMSO, London.

22. J Robinson, *How To Handle Your Drink*, Cedar/Mandarin, London, (1994), 105–106.

23. J Evans (ed.), *Good Beer Guide 1995*, CAMRA, St Albans, (1995).

24. W M Attenborough, *Ferment* (Newsletter of the Institute of Brewing), (1988), *1*, [2], 40–44.

25. R C Denney, Proc. 12th Int. Conf. (1992), 1506–1512.

26. S B Rosalki, 'Alcoholism – an Overview' in *Clinical Biochemistry of Alcoholism*, S B Rosalki (ed.), Churchill Livingstone, Edinburgh, (1984), 3–19.

27. A S R Sinton, *J. Forensic Science*, (1960), *1*, 21–23.

28. E Bogen, *J. Amer. Medic. Assoc.*, (1927), *89*, 1508–1511.

29. H Ward Smith, 'Methods for Determining Alcohol' in *Methods Foren. Sci.*, (1965), *4*, 53.

Chapter 2 – Alcohol in the Human Body

1. C S Lieber, *Scientific American*, (1976), *234*, [3], 25–33.

2. C S Lieber, *Brit. J. Alcohol and Alcoholism*, (1980), *15*, [3], 95.

3. R C Denney, 'Addiction, Nutrition and Health', in *Getting the Most out of Food*, Van den Burghs & Jurgens Ltd., Burgess Hill, (1982), 65–90.

4. R M Julien, *A Primer of Drug Action*, 7th edn., W H Freeman, New York, (1995), 66.

5. J Robinson, *How To Handle Your Drink*, Cedar/Mandarin, London, (1994), 86–87.

6. H J Walls & A R Brownlie, *Drink, Drugs and Driving*, 2nd edn., Sweet & Maxwell/W Green and Son, London and Edinburgh, (1985), 39.

7. U Loos & U Heifer, Proc. 8th Int. Conf. (1980), 1087–1098.

8. R C Denney, 'Measuring Alcohol', in *Clinical Biochemistry of Alcoholism*, S B Rosalki (ed.), Churchill Livingstone, Edinburgh, (1984), 51–64.

9. J P Payne, D W Hill & N W King, *Brit. Med. J.*, (1966), [1], 196.

10. W Froentjes, Proc. 3rd Int. Conf. (1962), 179–188.

11. S Kaye & E L Cardona, Proc. 4th Int. Conf. (1965), 178.

12. J P Payne, D W Hill & D G L Wood, *Nature*, (1968), *217*, 963–964.

13. G L S Pawan, *Nature*, (1968), *218*, 966.

14. G L S Pawan, *Medical Journal*, (1969), [350], 7.

15. H Ward Smith, 'Methods for Determining Alcohol', in *Methods Foren. Sci.*, (1965), *4*, 30.

16. R M Julien, *A Primer of Drug Action*, 7th edn., W H Freeman, New York, (1995), 65–67.

17. H J Walls & A R Brownlie, *Drink, Drugs and Driving*, 2nd edn., Sweet & Maxwell/W Green and Son, London and Edinburgh, (1985), 19.

18. R C Denney, Proc. 13th Int. Conf. (1995), 573–576.

19. D K Damkot, Proc. 8th Int. Conf. (1980), 923–937.

20. B Knight, *Simpson's Forensic Medicine*, 10th edn., Edward Arnold, London, (1991), 276.

21. For examples see: *Sevenoaks Chronicle* (1978), 14 Jan., and *Daily Telegraph* (1978), 15 March.

22. G Edwards et al, *Alcohol Policy and the Public Good*, Oxford University Press, Oxford, (1994), 168–186.

23. R Andreasson, *Widmark's Micromethod and Swedish Legislation on Alcohol and Traffic*, The Information Centre for Traffic Safety, Stockholm, (1986).

24. A R W Forrest, *J. Foren. Sci. Soc.*, (1986), *26*, 249–252.

25. D S Miller, J L Stirling & J Yudkin, *Nature*, (1966), 1051.

26. A H Beckett, M Mitchard & A Saunders, *Autocar*, (1971), 19 August, 34.

27. R C Denney & W Edwards, unpublished results from London Borough of Greenwich 1977 Christmas Road Safety Campaign.

28. P Ozorio, *J. Traffic Medicine*, (1981), *9*, [3], 38.

29. J Kirby, K Maull & W Fain, Proc. 11th Int. Conf. (1989), 328–331.

30. E J Calabrese, *Alcohol Interactions with Drugs and Chemicals*, Lewis Publications Inc., Chelsea, Michigan, (1991), 13.

Chapter 3 – Accidents on the Road

1. M W Perrine, R C Peck & J C Fell, 'Epidemiologic Perspectives on Drunk Driving', in *Background Papers,* US Dept of Health & Human Services, Washington DC, (1989), 37.

2. W D S McLay (ed.), *Clinical Forensic Medicine,* Pinter Publishers, London, (1990), 107.

3. R L Holcomb, *J. Amer. Med. Assoc.,* (1938), *111,* 1076.

4. A T Pearson, *Med. J. Aust.,* (1957), *44,* 166.

5. W S Schmidt & R C Smart, *Quart. J. Study Alcohol,* (1959), *5,* 311.

6. W Haddon & V A Bradness, *J. Amer. Med. Assoc.,* (1959), *1969,* 1587.

7. G O Jeffcoate, *Brit. J. Addiction,* (1958), *54,* 81, and (1958), *55,* 37. See also N I Spriggs, *Brit. Med. J.,* (1956), 631.

8. M Vamosi, *Traffic Safety Research Review,* (1961), *4,* 8.

9. R F Borkenstein et al, 'The Role of the Drinking Driver', in *Traffic Accidents* (Report of the Grand Rapids Survey), Dept of Police Administration, Indiana University, (1964).

10. H-P Kruger, J Kazenwadel & M Vollrath, Proc. 13th Int. Conf. (1995), 222–230.

11. R F Borkenstein, at 1st International Conference on Drivers' Behaviour, Zurich, reported in *Alliance News,* (1974), 1 February.

12. B M Sweedler, Proc. 12th Int. Conf. (1992), 912–916.

13. J Duncan, unpublished data from Canberra, referred to in Proc. 6th Int. Conf. (1974), 782. See also A J McLean & O T Holubowycz, Proc. 8th Int. Conf. (1980), 113–123.

14. T Norstrom, Proc. 8th Int. Conf. (1980), 1231–1246.

15. *Lex Report on Motoring,* Lex Services plc, London, (1994); see also *Alcohol Concern,* (1994), *9,* [1], 8.

16. J A Waller, Proc. 6th Int. Conf. (1974), 7.

17. J H W Burrell, Proc. 6th Int. Conf. (1974), 782.

18. J T Tonge, *Post-mortem Blood Alcohol Levels in Road Accident Victims*, National Road Safety Symposium, Department of Transport, Canberra, Australia, (1972).

19. H Malin et al., Proc. 9th Int. Conf. (1983), 903–913.

20. A B Clayton, P E McCarthy & J M Breen, *The Male Driver, Characteristics of the Offender and his Offence*, TRRL Supplementary Report No. 600, Dept of the Environment, London, (1980).

21. V J Storie, *The Role of Alcohol and Human Factors in Road Accidents*, at 5th Int. Conf. of the International Association for Accident and Traffic Medicine and the 3rd International Conference on Drug Abuse, published by TRRL, Dept of the Environment, London, (1975).

22. *Fatal Accident Reporting System 1990*, US Dept of Transportation, Washington DC, (1991), 183.

23. *Road Accidents Great Britain 1993*, Transport Research Laboratory, HMSO, London, (1994).

24. J D McCarthy & D S Harvey, 'Independent Citizen Advocacy – The Past and the Prospects', in *Surgeon General's Workshop on Drunk Driving*, US Dept of Health and Human Services, Washington DC, (1988), 247–260.

25. L R Sutton, Proc. 12th Int. Conf. (1992), 178–181.

26. B E Sabey & P J Codling, Proc. 6th Int. Conf. (1974), 73.

27. P J Codling & P Samson, *Blood Alcohol in Road Fatalities Before and After the Road Safety Act (1967)*, TRRL Supplementary Report 45 UC, Dept of the Environment, HMSO, London, (1974), 9.

28. J T Everest, Proc. 12th Int. Conf. (1992), 924–932.

29. *ICADTS Reporter*, (1993), *4*, [1], 1.

30. R F Turk et al., Proc. 6th Int. Conf. (1974), 597.

31. R D Blomberg et al., *A Comparison of Alcohol Involvement in Pedestrians and Pedestrian Casualties,* Dunlap & Associates, Darein, Connecticut, (1979).

32. T Bajanowski, P Kunz & B Brinkmann, *J. Traffic Med.,* (1994), *22,* [1], 33–38.

33. R C Denney, *Alcohol Concern,* (1992), *7,* [5], 16–17.

34. P R Marques & R B Voas, *J. Traffic Med.,* (1995), *23,* [2], 77–85.

Chapter 4 – Which Legal Limit?

1. H Ward Smith, 'Methods for Determining Alcohol', *Methods Foren. Sci.*, (1965), *4*, 30.

2. M Hebbelinck, Proc. 3rd Int. Conf. (1962), 136–139. See also E J D Ogden, I Cairns & E Curry, Proc. 13th Int. Conf. (1995), 627–632.

3. L Goldberg & J D J Havard, *Research on the Effects of Alcohol and Drugs on Driver Behaviour*, OECD Report, Paris, (1968).

4. L Goldberg, *Acta Physiol. Scand.*, (Supplement 16), (1943), *5*, 1.

5. J Pauwels & W Helsen, Proc. 12th Int. Conf. (1992), 637–642.

6. J Cohen, E J Dearnaley & C E M Hansel, *Brit. Med. J.*, (1958), 1438.

7. 'Motor Vehicle Accidents', Organisation Section, American Medical Association, *J. Amer. Med. Assoc.*, (1957), *163*, 1149.

8. M W Perrine, R C Peck & J C Fell, 'Epidemiologic Perspectives on Drunk Driving', in *Background Papers,* US Dept of Health & Human Services, Washington DC, (1989), 50.

9. *Relation of Alcohol to Road Accidents*, British Medical Association, London, (1960).

10. B B Coldwell et al., *Report of Committee on Alcohol and Driving*, Canadian Society of Forensic Science, (1962), 28 October.

11. *Lion Intoximeter 3000 Operator Handbook*, Lion Laboratories Ltd., Barry, Wales, (1982), 16.

12. J D J Havard, Proc. 4th Int. Conf. (1965), 17–25.

13. R C Denney, Proc. 13th Int. Conf. (1995), 573–576.

Chapter 5 – Roadside Breath Tests

1. E Bogen, *J. Amer. Med. Assoc.*, (1927), *89*, 1508.

2. R N Harger, E B Lamb & H R Halpien, *J. Amer. Med. Assoc.*, (1938), *110*, 779. See also US Patents 2,062,785 and 2,867,511.

3. W W Jetter, M Moore and G C Forrester, *Amer. J. Clin. Pathol.*, (1941), *11*, 75.

4. J Berkebile, *J. Chem. Educ.*, (1954), *31*, 380.

5. L A Greenberg & F W Keator, *Quart. J. Stud. on Alcohol*, (1941), *2*, 57.

6. H W Haggard & L A Greenberg, *J. Pharmacol. and Experimen. Therap.*, (1934), *52*, 137.

7. K Grosskopf, *Angew. Chem.*, (1951), *63*, 306.

8. M Dragërwerk, German Patent 932,750, (1959).

9. M Dragërwerk, German Patent 1,037,726, (1961).

10. British Patent 1,143,818.

11. K Hinsberg, *Deut. Z. Ges. Gerichtl. Med.*, (1939), *31*, 194.

12. K Grosskopf, Proc. 3rd Int. Conf. (1962), 281–285.

13. M Day, G G Muir & J Watling, *Nature*, (1968), *219*, 1051.

14. Blennerhassett, (1976), 15.

15. G J Kleywegt & W L Driessen, *Chem. Brit.*, (1988), *24*, [5], 447–450.

16. H L Gruber & H Huck, Third International Symposium on Fuel Cells, Brussels, Belgium, (1969), 16–20 June.

17. *Lion Alcolmeter S–L2 Operator Handbook*, Lion Laboratories plc., (1987).

18. D Hunt et al., Proc. 9th Int. Conf. (1983), 639–652.

19. A W Jones & K A Jönsson, Proc. 12th Int. Conf. (1992), 423–429.

Chapter 6 – Evidential Breath Testing

1. R F Borkenstein, *Traffic Digest and Review*, (1954), [11], 2.

2. R F Borkenstein, British Patent 821,013, (1959).

3. J G Scroggie, Proc. 3rd Int. Conf. (1962), 272–276.

4. B H Fox, J Lower & M W Fox, Proc. 3rd Int. Conf. (1962), 261–271.

5. V J Emerson et al., *J. Forens. Sci. Soc.*, (1980), *20*, 3–70.

6. M L Moberg, E M Wilson & P J Meredith, US Patent 3,338,087.

7. M H Breen, K F Silver & D S Pearce, Proc. 6th Int. Conf. (1974), 549.

8. R A Harte, *J. Forensic Sci.*, (1971), *16*, 4 and 593.

9. D G Hutson, Proc. 9th Int. Conf. (1983), 653–660.

10. M D J Isaacs et al, *Field Trial of Three Substantive Breath Alcohol Testing Instruments*, HMSO, London, (1982).

11. BBC Checkpoint, Radio 4, (1983), 20 April.

12. *Daily Express*, various issues (1984), March/April.

13. Transport Act 1981, HMSO, London, (1981).

14. M D J Isaacs & D J Hunt, *A Survey of Analyses of Breath and Blood Samples Provided by Subjects within the Option Range*, Home Office, London, (1984).

15. R C Denney, *J. Forens. Sci. Soc.*, (1990), *30*, [6], 357–361.

16. R Gill et al., *Med. Sci. Law*, (1991), *31*, [3], 187–220.

17. R C Denney & P M Williams, Proc. 10th Int. Conf. (1986), 355–358.

18. P J Gomm & C G Broster, Proc. 12th Int. Conf. (1992), 1513–1521; and *Evidential Breath Alcohol Testing Instruments*, HMSO, London, (1994).

19. R C Denney, *Autocar*, (1978), 1 April, 34–36.

20. Blennerhasset, (1976), 61.

Chapter 7 – Blood and Urine Tests

1. R C Denney, Proc. 13th Int. Conf. (1995), 573–576.

2. W W Jetter, *Quart. J. Stud. Alcohol*, (1941), *2*, 512. See also *Chem. Test Intoxic.*, (1959), 7.

3. W Froentjes, Proc. 3rd. Int. Conf. (1962), 179–188.

4. J P Payne et al., *Brit. Med. J.*, (1966), [1], 196.

5. B M Wright, *Nature*, (1968), *218*, 1263.

6. G Chedd, *New Scientist*, (1968), 577.

7. R C Denney, *The Truth About Breath Tests*, Nelson, London, (1970), Chapter 6, 40.

8. M Nicloux, *Z. Physiol. Chem.*, (1905), *43*, 476.

9. H Ward Smith, 'Methods for Determining Alcohol', Chapter 1 in *Methods Foren. Sci.* (1965), *4*.

10. D W Kent-Jones, *J. Royal Inst. Chem.*, (1957), 491.

11. R C Denney, *Chemistry in Britain*, (1970), *6*, 533–535.

12. J F Marten, Proc. 3rd Int. Conf. (1962), 226–230.

13. R C Denney & P Daga, Proc. 9th Int. Conf. (1983), 299–306.

14. R C Denney, J Glover & M A Russell, Proc. 11th Int. Conf. (1989), 809–811.

15. R C Denney et al., Proc. 12th Int. Conf. (1992), 438–444.

16. H Heizer, in *The Analysis of Drugs of Abuse*, T A Gough (ed.), J Wiley & Sons, Chichester, (1991), 23–92.

17. B L Glendenning & R A Harvey, *J. Forensic Sci.*, (1969), *14*, 136.

18. R C Denney, *A Dictionary of Chromatography*, 2nd edn., Macmillan, London, (1982), 105.

Chapter 8 – The Legal Aspects of Drink-Driving

1. G E Hall, 'Medicolegal Aspects of Chemical Tests', Chapter VIII in *Chem. Test. Intoxic.*, (1959), 65.

2. *Traffic Safety Facts 1992*, US Dept of Transportation, Washington DC, (1994), 170–171.

3. Road Safety Act 1967, Part I, HMSO, London, (1967).

4. Road Traffic Act 1972, HMSO, London, (1972).

5. P Halnan & J Spencer, *Wilkinson's Road Traffic Offences*, 11th edn., Oyez Longman, London, (1982).

6. *Regina v Jones* (EJM), (1970) 1 ALL ER 209.

7. T McCabe, *Drive Magazine*, (1978), 23 August.

8. Blennerhassett, (1976), 6.

9. R C Denney, *Chemistry & Industry*, (1976), 15 May, 424.

10. *Consultative Document on Drinking and Driving*, Dept of Transport, London, (1979), December.

11. R C Denney, *Comments on the Consultative Paper on Drinking and Driving*, (1980), March.

12. The Justices' Clerks Society, *Observations on the Department of Transport's Consultative Document on Drinking and Driving*, (1980), March.

13. Transport Act 1981, HMSO, London, (1981).

14. P Halnan & J Spencer, *Wilkinson's Road Traffic Offences*, 1st Supplement to the 11th edn., Oyez Longman, London, (1983).

15. W H D Morgan, Proc. 8th Int. Conf. (1980), 195–202.

16. M D J Isaacs & D J Hunt, *A Survey of Analyses of Breath and Blood Samples Provided by Subjects within the Option Range*, Home Office, London, (1984).

17. W Paton, P G W Cobb & M D G Dabbs, *Report on Breath Alcohol Measuring Instruments*, HMSO, London, (1985).

18. *A Comparative Study of Breath Test Machines and Blood Alcohol Analysis Results*, The Royal Society of Chemistry, London, (1985).

19. *Evidential Breath Alcohol Testing Instruments – A Guide to Type Approval Procedures*, HMSO & FSS, London, (1995), 9.

20. R C Denney, *J. Foren. Sci. Soc.*, (1990), *30*, [6], 357–361.

21. *Kierman v Wilcox* (1972) RTR 270.

22. N J Ley, *Drink Driving Law and Practice*, Sweet & Maxwell, London, (1993).

23. *Murray v DPP*, Law Report, *The Independent*, (1993), 12 February, 26.

24. R C Denney, *New Law Journal*, (1986), *136*, [6273], 923–924.

25. Transport Amendment Act (No. 3) 1978, sections 7 and 8, New Zealand.

Chapter 9 – Alcohol and Other Accidents

1. *Alcohol Concern*, (1991), *6*, [5], 8. See also *Daily Telegraph*, (1995), 18 September, 6.

2. S B Rosalki, 'Identifying the Alcoholic', in *Clinical Biochemistry of Alcoholism'*, S B Rosalki (ed.), Churchill Livingstone, London, (1984), 65–92.

3. J L'Hoste & L Papoz, Proc. 9th Int. Conf. (1983), 841–858.

4. R C Denney, 'Danger from the Drinker at Work', *General & Municipal Workers Herald*, (1977), June, 5.

5. G P Williams & G T Brake, *Drink in Great Britain 1900–1979*, Edsall, London, (1980).

6. J Godard, 'Alcohol and Occupation', in *Alcohol Problems in Employment*, More & Plant (eds.), Croom & Helm, Beckenham, (1981), Chapter 6, 111.

7. B Metz & F Marcoux, *Reveu de l'Alcoholisme*, (1960), [3], 6; and (1960), [4], 6.

8. G Edwards et al., *Clients of Alcoholism Information Centres*, National Council on Alcoholism, (1967).

9. G Edwards et al, *Alcohol Policy and the Public Good*, Oxford University Press, (1944), 216.

10. B Braine (Chairman), *Report on the Working Party on Alcohol and Work*, 3rd edn., National Council on Alcoholism, (1978).

11. P B Beaumont & S J Allsop, Beverage Report, *Occupational Health and Safety*, (1983), October, 25–27.

12. M A Argyropoulos-Grisanos, *Effects of Alcohol on the Performance of some Industrial Tests*, PhD Thesis, Polytechnic of Wales, (1980).

13. M A Argyropoulos-Grisanos & P J L Hawkins, *Alcohol and Industrial Accidents*, Christian Economic and Social Research Foundation, London, (1980).

14. M Schreiber, Proc. 12th Int. Conf. (1992), 96–107.

15. R C Denney & R Johnson, *Proc. Nutrition Soc.*, (1984), *43*, 265–270. See also M Shain, *Accident Analysis and Prevention*, (1982), *14*, [3], 239.

16. J E Hall, Proc. 13th Int. Conf. (1995), 3–10.

17. S Barlay, *Aircrash Detective*, Hamish Hamilton, (1969), 281.

18. C R Harper & W R Albers, Proc. 4th Int. Conf. (1965), 230.

19. B M Sweedler, Proc. 9th Int. Conf. (1983), 1347–1355.

20. E G Aksnes, *Aviation Medicine*, (1954), *25*, 680.

21. Reported by L Gross, *How Much Is Too Much*, Ballantine, New York, (1983), 31–32.

22. C E Billings et al, reported in *ICADTS Reporter*, (1991), *2*, [3], 2.

23. D Beatty, *The Human Factor in Aircraft Accidents*, Secker & Warburg, (1969).

24. D Leigh, 'Tube Men Who Drink and Drive', *Evening Standard*, (1978), 11 October, 1.

25. M A Manello & F J Seaman, *Prevalence, Costs and Handling of Drinking Problems on Seven Railroads*, DOT-DSC-1375, Dept of Transportation, Washington DC, (1979).

26. Reported in *Daily Mirror*, (1982), 18 February.

27. Reported in *Daily Telegraph*, (1983), 10 May.

28. R C Denney, *Alcohol Concern*, (1992), *7*, [5], 16–17.

29. *Alcohol Concern*, (1994), *9*, [2], 5.

30. Sections 7, 8 & 20, Health and Safety at Work Act 1974, HMSO, London, (1974).

31. F Husinec, Proc. 12th Int. Conf. (1992), 1007–1010.

32. B Greene (ed.), 'Alcohol & Aquatics', *Proceedings of the Symposium, (1977), 13th May*, Royal Life Saving Society Canada, (1977).

33. O Arner, *Brit. J. Addict.*, (1973), *68*, 185–189.

34. V D Pleuckhahn, *Med. Sci. Law*, (1977), *17*, [14], 246–250.

35. *Drownings in the British Isles 1983*, Royal Life Saving Society, London, (1984).

36. P E Dietz & S P Baker, *J. Public Health*, (1974), *64*, 303.

37. J Pikkarainen & A Penttil, Proc. 11th Int. Conf. (1989), 283–290.

38. K J B Rix, 'Alcohol Problems and the Fishing Industry in NE Scotland', in B Hore & M Plant (eds.), *Alcohol Problems in Employment*, Croom Helm, Beckenham, (1981), 82–87.

39. *Report of the Committee of Enquiry into Trawler Safety*, Board of Trade, HMSO, London, (1969).

40. Reported in *Daily Telegraph*, (1980), 21 February.

41. Reported in *Daily Telegraph*, (1991), 9 December.

42. Reported in *The Independent*, (1991), 28 November.

Chapter 10 – Alcohol, Education and the Future

1. J Medlund & J Fell, Proc. 13th Int. Conf. (1995), 596–604.

2. I Davies & D Raistrick, *Dealing With Drink*, British Broadcasting Corporation, London, (1981).

3. A B Clayton, Proc. 13th Int. Conf. (1995), 282–285.

4. D W Collier et al, Proc. 13th Int. Conf. (1995), 673–677.

5. J O'Connor, *The Young Drinkers*, Tavistock Publications, London, (1978).

6. J Robinson, *How To Handle Your Drink*, Cedar/Mandarin, London, (1994), 184.

7. G Lanagan, *National Council on Alcoholism News*, (1983), Autumn, 2.

8. V Marks, *Clinics in Endocrinology and Metabolism*, (1978), *333*, [2], 7.

9. G Jones, *Daily Mail*, (1989), 4 December.

10. R C Denney & R Johnson, *Proc. Nutrition Soc.*, (1984), *43*, 265–270.

11. O H Drummer, Proc. 13th Int. Conf. (1995), 426–429.

12. H Gjerde, K M Beylich & J Mörland, *Accident Analysis & Prevention*, (1993), *24*, [4], 479–483.

13. D Brockoff et al, *The New England J. Medicine*, (1994), [8], 331.

14. P M Williams, Proc. 12th Int. Conf. (1992), 1491–1497.

15. R J Breakspere, A Porter & L Nadillo, Proc. 11th Int. Conf. (1989), 611–614.

INDEX